Behavior Research Fund
Monographs

BRAIN MECHANISMS AND
INTELLIGENCE

BRAIN MECHANISMS
AND INTELLIGENCE

A QUANTITATIVE STUDY OF
INJURIES TO THE BRAIN

K. S. LASHLEY

HAFNER PUBLISHING COMPANY
New York and London
1964

Originally published 1929
by University of Chicago Press

Printed and Published by
HAFNER PUBLISHING CO., INC.
31 East 10th Street
New York 3, N.Y.

Library of Congress Card Catalogue Number: 63-18172

© Copyright 1963 by Hafner Publishing Company, Inc.

Printed in U.S.A. by
NOBLE OFFSET PRINTERS, INC.
NEW YORK 3, N. Y.

INTRODUCTION TO REPRINT 1963

The publishing in 1929 of the late K. S. Lashley's book, *Brain Mechanisms and Intelligence* marked the beginning of a concerted experimental effort to localize cortical functions more accurately than had been previously attempted. The subtitle, *A Quantitative Study of Injuries to the Brain,* indicated the method of approach. *Brains of Rats and Men* (1926) by C. Judson Herrick had emphasized the interest in this subject. Herrick utilized much of Lashley's work on rats which was then in the journals. Twenty years later Ward C. Halstead's *Brain and Intelligence* presented a similar picture for man. Professor Halstead presented a quantitative study, chiefly of the frontal lobes of man using case histories of men in which known cortical lesions occurred.

Within the last few years many symposia have been held throughout the world concerning the brain and its relation to intelligence, behavior, consciousness, learning etc. It is of importance especially to the younger workers in this field that Lashley's book should be made available. Professor Lashley was a physiological psychologist of rare abilities. He began this concerted attack upon the study of the mind. In his paper, "Cerebral Organization and Behavior" (1958—Research Publications—Association for Research in Nervous and Mental Diseases) he concluded that "mind is a complex organization, held together by the interaction of processes and by time scales of memory, centered about the body image." He further emphasized that mental phenomena must be subjected to as rigorous an analysis as the neurological and he anticipated that critical study would reveal that the combination might offer two aspects of a common structure-function.

Lashley's concern with the nature of intelligence was inclusive as approached by this biologist. He concluded that the concept of intelligence was becoming essentially a statistical one. In his judgment the broad theory of learning and of intelligence was in a state of confusion. He saw certain similarities between learning and intelligence and it was due to his methods in the study of the rat brain which aided him in rationalizing these similarities.

It may take many generations of biologically-trained psychologists to fully understand and appreciate the differences that exist between the rat mind-brain and the human mind-brain. Lashley's *Brain Mechanisms and Intelligence* is an excellent starting point for this study. It is, therefore, imperative that we should have more copies available to those now working in this rapidly-expanding field in which the man-made thinking machine (computer) may yet teach us how our own thinking machine works.

Lawrence, Kansas   PAUL G. ROOFE
October, 1936   *University of Kansas*

FOREWORD

The late William Osler once said that as the nineteenth century had been characterized by great advances in the physical sciences and in medicine, the twentieth century would undoubtedly show equal progress in mental sciences. The first quarter of the twentieth century has borne out his prophecy through the remarkable interest evidenced by scientists and laymen alike in the problem of man, his mental characteristics, and his social relations. But as so often happens where the interest is great and achievement is moderate, one does not know where to begin. In such situations there are always individuals wiser than the rest, who suggest that perhaps these are problems which have no solution and that we are in the position of the mice who agreed to the desirability of attaching a bell to the cat but could find no way of accomplishing it.

But one of the most important characteristics of man is courage, and science has long since given up the belief in impossibilities. There may still be questions to which there are no answers, but the scientist must prove this in each instance before he will accept it.

This spirit of adventure and this enthusiasm for attacking the mysteries of nature, together with the need for scientific information in regard to the problems of human behavior and human relations, inspired a group of public-spirited citizens of Chicago to organize a campaign to secure subscriptions for a fund known and incorporated as the "Behavior Research Fund," to be devoted to research in problems of human behavior.

In October, 1926, this fund made it possible to secure a staff of specialists in the fields which have a bearing on problems of behavior and conduct, such as psychology, sociology, anthropology, education, physiology, and medicine. This staff, freed from teaching and administrative duties, were thus enabled to devote all their time to research. Through the generosity of the State of Illinois, the headquarters and clinical material of the

Institute for Juvenile Research were made available to the Behavior Research Fund.

With the conclusion of its third year, the Behavior Research Fund herewith presents the first volume of a series of monographs, each the report of the results of research in one of the fields mentioned.

The monograph of Professor Karl S. Lashley is the first fruit of this enterprise. It may puzzle some that the approach to human behavior should lead through such an apparent bypath, but a frontal attack is not necessarily the most effective. Nature's secrets sometimes yield to an ambuscade.

Another point of significance is to be discerned in this volume, to wit: the old academic liberty of the Renaissance is the greatest safeguard to successful scientific enterprise. In this day of superorganization, of mergers, and of quantity production, one sees the practical executive reaching out for control of scientific investigation and hoping to achieve fundamental discoveries by sheer weight of funds and of mass formations. But science, like art, does not yield to such advances. Genius must have freedom to show itself. This ideal of liberty, of freedom for the scientist, has guided the subscribers of the Behavior Research Fund and its trustees in their attitude toward the scientific workers on its staff.

The importance of this monograph is not to be regarded as a commitment on the part of the Behavior Research Fund to continue to produce similarly brilliant results. Academic liberty requires loyalty to the scientist not only when he succeeds but when his research turns out a blank. We are proud that after only three years of work a monograph of this significance can be presented.

HERMAN M. ADLER

PREFACE

The experiments reported in the following pages are a continuation of a program, outlined some years ago, for an analysis of the neural mechanisms which play a part in learning. As the work has progressed, it has become increasingly clear that the associative or mnemonic process cannot be sharply distinguished, at least in experimental procedure, from other psychological processes. Logically we may distinguish the solution of problems by rational analysis or random activity, the fixation of the solution in memory (the "ecphoric" process of Semon), the retention of the memories, and their recall under appropriate conditions. But our experimental methods have rarely, if ever, dealt with these processes in isolation. In particular, the studies of animal learning have confused the issues, offering as explanations of fixation theories which can apply only to the mechanism of problem-solving and ignoring many of the complexities of behavior which appear in the learning even of animals low in the evolutionary scale. These complexities, for which evidence is accumulating from many sources, are incompatible with simple theories of conditioning or of learning by the elimination of errors, and confront us with a far more difficult problem than is admitted by such theories. In many ways they suggest the behavior which we designate as "intelligent," and it has seemed worth while to attempt to relate the results of the present experiments to the broader problems of intelligence rather than to consider them only from their limited bearing upon the mechanism of fixation of habits.

The whole theory of learning and of intelligence is in confusion. We know at present nothing of the organic basis of these functions and little enough of either the variety or uniformities of their expression in behavior. The concepts are so poorly defined that it has not been possible even to imagine a program of physiological research which seemed likely to reveal more than superficial relationships. Thus there is really no starting-point for a constructive analysis of the neurological data from these experiments. I have attempted to interpret the results in relation to current theories and have perhaps made wider applications than their limited character justifies. The excuse for this is that it serves better to emphasize the possibilities of the method. The experiments constitute the first attempt to apply quantitative methods to both neurological and behavior data. They show that the method is capable of giving consistent results relevant to the fundamental problems of the nature and mechanisms and learning and problem-solving.

The inferences drawn from the experiments seem to be for the most part clearly indicated. Their uncertainty lies rather in the lack of complete statistical reliability of the data and in the limited number of situations studied. To remedy this defect would require a repetition of the experiments with perhaps five times as many animals and the extension of the tests to thirty or more well-selected problems—a twenty-year program at the present rate of progress. Any final conclusions must therefore await the accumulation of far more evidence than we have at present; yet some of the implications of these experiments are clear, and their value as a basis for a more definite formulation of the problems justifies the attempt at interpretation.

The experiments in the following study were not originally planned as a unitary attack upon a single phase of the learning problem but have developed out of the necessity of seeking explanations for facts which have evolved as the work progressed. The study of retention of the maze habit after cerebral lesions was first in point of time. It was undertaken primarily to discover whether or not the quantitative relationship previously found between cerebral injury and the retention of the habit of brightness discrimination would hold for a habit of a different type. It gave the result, unexpected in the light of earlier work, that relearning of the maze after cerebral insult might require many times more practice than initial learning. This led to the series of experiments dealing with the influence of cerebral lesions upon the initial formation of a variety of habits, which are reported as logically first. The necessity for controls of the sensory and motor components of the habits called for other experiments on animals with sense privation and with lesions to the cerebellum and spinal cord. These are essential for the interpretation of all the other data and so are summarized separately after the report of the two major experiments. Taken altogether, the experiments give a fairly consistent and comprehensive mass of data bearing upon the influence of cerebral destruction upon ability to solve and remember a variety of problems.

All of the lesions to the brain which are included in the present study involve both hemispheres, and they are for the most part symmetrical. We know little of the interrelations of the two hemispheres. With the development of handedness and speech in man there have come certain specializations which are probably absent in lower animals, yet it is possible that even in the rat lesions restricted to one hemisphere will give results of an entirely different sort from those reported here.

The greater part of the experiment dealing with retention of the maze habit after cerebral insult was completed in the laboratory of the Department of Psychology of the University of Minnesota. I am indebted to the University for grants in support of the work and for unusual opportunities for research.

The remainder of the work has been carried out under the Behavior Research Fund. I am indebted to Professor C. J. Herrick for several critical discussions of the results and for assistance and advice in interpreting the serial sections of some of the brains which presented unusual difficulties.

K. S. LASHLEY

CHICAGO, ILLINOIS

CONTENTS

CHAPTER   PAGE

I. THEORIES AND PROBLEMS   1
Psychological Theories of Intelligence   1
Neurological Theories   3
The Problem of Intelligence in Experiments with Animals . .   12
Object of the Present Experiments   14

II. GENERAL METHODS   16
Surgical and Anatomical   16
Graphic and Statistical   18
Reliability of the Methods   20
Difficulties of Interpretation in Studies of Brain Injuries   . .   23

III. THE INFLUENCE OF CEREBRAL LESIONS UPON THE CAPACITY
TO LEARN   27
Problems and Special Methods   28
Deterioration of Operated Animals Shown by Massed Records   35
Permanence of the Deterioration   48
The Influence of the Locus of Injury upon Retardation in
Learning   49
The Relation between the Degree of Deterioration and the Ex-
tent of Injury   61
Cerebral Function as Conditioned by the Complexity of the
Problem   70

IV. THE INFLUENCE OF BRAIN INJURIES UPON RETENTIVENESS   .   76

V. THE COURSE OF LEARNING IN DETERIORATED CASES   . . .   81

VI. THE EFFECTS OF CEREBRAL LESION SUBSEQUENT TO THE FOR-
MATION OF THE MAZE HABIT: LOCALIZATION OF THE HABIT   .   86
Special Methods   89
General Plan of Experimentation   89
Relation of the Locus of Injury to the Retention of the Maze
Habit   91
The Influence of the Size of the Lesion upon Postoperative
Retention   100

VII. THE RELATION OF REDUCED LEARNING ABILITY TO SENSORY
AND MOTOR DEFECTS   109
The Effects of Sense-Privation upon Maze Learning   . . .   110
Types of Deterioration in Relation to Cerebral Lesions   . .   116

CONTENTS

CHAPTER   PAGE

VIII. DISCUSSION OF EXPERIMENTAL RESULTS 120
      Summary of Data 120
      Non-specificity of Cerebral Structures for Learning 122
      The Synapse in Retention 125
      The Mass Factor in Cerebral Function 127

IX. THE NATURE OF THE DETERIORATION FOLLOWING CEREBRAL
      LESIONS 132
      Significance of Different Results in the Formation of Maze and
        Discrimination Habits 132
      Retardation Not Specific for the Maze 138

X. COMPARISON OF THE RAT WITH OTHER FORMS 142
      Cerebral Function in the Dog 142
      Cerebral Function in the Monkey 149
      Correspondences and Differences in Cerebral Function in the
        Rat and Man 151

XI. NEURAL MECHANISMS IN ADAPTIVE BEHAVIOR 157
      Theories of Cerebral Localization Not Explanatory 161
      The Reflex Theory Inadequate 163
      Dynamic Theories 164
      Suggestions toward a Theory of Neural Organization . . . 166
      Implications of the Data for Theories of Intelligence . . . 172

SUMMARY 175

BIBLIOGRAPHY 177

INDEX 185

CHAPTER I

THEORIES AND PROBLEMS

In the interest to measure intelligence and to deduce from the results of measurement some conception of the nature of the function, the problem of the physiological basis of complex adaptive behavior has been largely ignored in recent discussions. This is perhaps due less to a lack of interest in the fundamental mechanisms of intelligent actions than to a feeling that our knowledge of the functions of the brain is too slight either to suggest any positive clues as to the nature of intelligence or to set any limits to speculation based upon data derived from other sources. We have thus a variety of psychological theories of intelligence, each of which involves definite implications concerning the nature of the underlying brain processes, but in none of which an attempt has been made to trace out these implications and to evaluate the theory in terms of their probability.

PSYCHOLOGICAL THEORIES OF INTELLIGENCE

Many of the psychological theories of intelligence are decidedly animistic in trend and fall wholly outside the scope of scientific treatment. Definitions of intelligence as purposive either save the latter word at the expense of its accepted meaning (Tolman, 1925 *a, b;* Herrick, 1926 *b*) or deny the validity of causal explanation in relation to it (McDougall, 1923), and in neither case require special consideration in a deterministic world.

The theories which seek a naturalistic interpretation of intelligence fall roughly into four classes, which, however, are not clearly distinct in their neurological implications.

1. The unit factory theory, developed chiefly by students of heredity, recognizes intelligence as a single variable, at least in its genetic behavior. The theory does not rule out special capacities but suggests that these may be developed to some extent independently of the general capacity which pervades all behavior.

There has been no attempt to relate the function to any brain mechanisms. Seemingly the variable might correlate either with the development of a special co-ordinating center, thus harmonizing with doctrines of localization, or with the general development of the brain as a whole. The latter in turn might involve complexity of anatomical structure or efficiency of physiological organization, such as delicacy of equilibrium among reaction systems. Assuming the independent development of special capacities, the theory would seem to be more in harmony with doctrines of restriction of intelligence to the activity of association centers than with the belief that the cerebrum acts either as a whole or by the summation of the specialized functions of its parts.

2. The "two-factor" theory of Spearman (1927) has much in common with the genetic theory, in assuming a general factor in addition to specific abilities. It differs in making more definite assumptions concerning the specific contributions of the general and special factors to particular abilities. Spearman is inclined to interpret the general factor as the total available nervous energy at the disposal of the individual, in spite of the opposition on the part of students of nerve conduction to any concept of general nervous energy.

3. In contrast to such views are those which look upon intelligence as an algebraic sum of diverse capacities.

Thorndike (1927) has given the clearest formulation of the aggregate theory of intelligence. He suggests that the quantity of intelligence in any individual is the result of the number of connections, existing or possible, within the nervous system.

Let c represent whatever anatomical or physiological fact corresponds to the possibility of forming one connection or association or bond between an idea or any part or aspect or feature thereof and a sequent idea or movement or any part or aspect or feature thereof. Then if individuals I, I_2, I_3, I_4, etc., differing in the number of c's which they possess but alike in other respects, are subjected to identical environments, the amount or degree of intellect which any one of them manifests, and the extent to which he manifests "higher" intellectual processes than the other individuals, will be closely proportional to the number of c's which he possesses. If we rank them by intelligence examination scores, the order will be that of the number of c's.

If we rank the intellectual processes in a scale from lower, such as mere information, to higher, such as reasoning, the individuals who manifest the highest processes will have the largest number of c's.

In addition to the number of connections available, Thorndike suggests that the "capacity of the neurones to act with reference to one another," by which he seems to mean the union of all connections in some common integration, may also be a factor in intelligence; and he mentions various motivating agents as further conditions for the expression of the potential intelligence determined by the number of bonds.

4. The configuration hypothesis. The conception of intelligence growing out of the work of the Gestalt school is evidently different from the foregoing, although it has not been elaborated in relation to the problem of individual differences. An intelligent act is one in which the elements of a situation are united in a significant configuration, and individual differences in intelligence result from the possession of fewer or more modes of relating experience. Thus Koffka (1925) describes the development of the child's intelligence in terms of the successive acquisition of such configurations as the object-name relation, prenumerical constructs, and the like. The theory seems to involve the conception that each increment of intelligence in the individual involves a qualitatively different organization from the last. This would outlaw the current conceptions of quantitative differences in intelligence, and the attempts to express the growth of intelligence upon a continuous scale. It implies also a distinct type of neurological theory, departing widely from the more generally accepted views of the fundamental nervous mechanisms and precluding any simple quantitative relationship between neural organization and intellectual level.

NEUROLOGICAL THEORIES

Neurologists of the last century were much interested in the nature of intelligence and, although their conceptions of the problem were less definite, or perhaps merely less technical, than the current psychological ones, they expressed the main theses of all the current psychological doctrines. Their theories represent three fairly distinct points of view. The weight of opinion favors one of these, but the actual evidence still leaves their relative value undetermined.

1. *Dynamic theory.*—Flourens (1842) maintained that intelligent behavior is an indivisible function of the activity of the entire cerebrum. He did not speculate concerning its mechanism beyond implying that it represented a summation of the energy of the whole organ.

The cerebral hemispheres are the sole organs for the perceptions and volitions. . . . . All perceptions and volitions have the same distribution in the hemispheres; the faculties of perceiving, understanding, and willing constitute a single function which is essentially unitary. . . . . Excitation of one point in the nervous system involves all others; there is community of reaction, of changes, of energy. Unity is the great principle which rules, is universal, dominates all. The nervous system forms a single unified system.

Goltz (1881) followed Flourens in contending that intelligence cannot be dissociated into subordinate functions having separate localization in the brain. He denied emphatically that the dementia produced in dogs by ablation of portions of the cerebral hemispheres is referable to any sort of a sensory defect, and considered that it is of essentially the same type after lesions to any area. He stresses the relation between the degree of dementia and the extent of destruction.

We may again affirm that every injury of the cortex of the two hemispheres seriously impairs the intelligence, has dementia as a consequence. The conclusion of Flourens that after partial removal of the cerebrum the intelligence is not reduced is only correct in part. After removal of the cortex of one hemisphere the intelligence is in many cases not noticeably influenced. But whenever both hemispheres are involved to an equal extent the disturbance of intelligence is significant and permanent. In general, one may affirm that the degree of dementia is proportionate to the spacial extent of the lesion. After removal of both posterior quadrants the dementia appears to be more striking than after removal of the anterior. But the surface of the former is appreciably greater than that of the latter. An animal with the posterior half of one hemisphere and the anterior half of the other destroyed approaches the mean between animals with the anterior and those with the posterior quadrants destroyed. The dementia after removal of three quadrants is severe and most severe of all after destruction of the four quadrants.

Attempting to define the nature of the dementia, Goltz was led to ascribe it to a general defect in attention rather than to a loss of any special systems of sensations or ideas. After cerebral lesions the animal is not able to attend exclusively to any one group of stimuli and so cannot integrate the stimuli intelligently. This definitely implies that intelligence is dependent upon some function of all parts of the cerebrum, a function which is qualitatively the same and varies only in quantity.

Loeb (1902) has been almost the only writer of the present century to uphold this view. He summarized his own results and those of Goltz, together with a few clinical cases, and found the evidence opposed to the restriction of "associative memory" to any part of the cerebrum. From various sources of evidence on the mutual influence of rhythmic activities of the nervous system he evolved a theory that cerebral integration consists of the establishment of functional periodicities among the parts of the cortex such that associations are called out by resonance. Different amounts of intelligence are dependent upon the degree of development of the resonating properties of the cerebrum.

Such views of the unitary nature of intelligence and the qualitatively similar participation of all parts of the cerebrum in the function have fallen completely into disrepute through the dominance of associationist doctrines in neurology and psychology and the accumulation of neurological evidence for specialization of parts of the cerebral cortex. Such views as those of Goltz seem incapable of particularization. We cannot apply them to explain the characteristics of loss in any form of dementia; and we can form no conception, on the basis of his observations, of how a unified mass of nervous tissue may function in diverse activities with a degree of efficiency solely proportional to its quantity. The theory is thus less satisfactory than the more analytic ones involving localization. The latter are therefore to be preferred unless the dynamic theory can be worked out in more detailed application to the facts or unless the evidence in favor of a unitary function becomes overwhelming.

2. *Theory of aggregation.*—A second theory, early expressed, was that derived by Munk (1909) from his work upon sensory

localization. Munk divided the cerebrum into a number of primary "sensory spheres"—visual, auditory, tactile, etc.—in each of which he believed the images and ideas associated with a single mode of sensation are stored and elaborated. Intelligence was conceived as the aggregate of all these products of the single sensory spheres, brought together by the manifold interconnections between them. ". . . . I considered the whole cerebral cortex, the aggregate of all the sensory spheres, to be the seat of the intelligence, which I defined as the combination and product of all the ideas arising from the sense-perceptions." For Munk the interconnections between the sensory spheres were adequate for the most complex integrations and there was no need for the postulation of any specialized association centers or areas devoted to the higher intellectual processes.

With this view Monakow (1914) to a certain extent concurs. He considers the evidence inadequate to establish any special intellectual function in the "association areas," and points out that whereas simple sensory and motor functions may be definitely localized, the more complex processes of memory involve the co-ordination of many diverse sensory and motor processes individually localized in diverse parts of the cortex and hence incapable of inclusion within any single insular area.

Between the adherents of this view and the proponents of the doctrine of special association areas controversy has raged continuously for the past fifty years.

3. *Theories of localization.*—Following the reaction against Gall's phrenology, Broadbent (1872) and Hitzig (1884) were the first to reassert the existence of specialized areas of the cerebrum particularly concerned with intelligence. Discussing Munk's position, Hitzig stated (1884):

I agree heartily that the intelligence—better called the store of ideas— is to be sought in all parts of the cortex—better again to say all parts of the brain. But I insist that abstract thinking demands a special organ and this I seek provisionally in the frontal lobes.

Such views received support from Flechsig's distinction between association and projection areas, although Flechsig emphasized the importance of the parietal rather than of the frontal area as the part chiefly concerned in intellectual activities; and the majority of recent writers has concurred in assigning great importance to the association areas in all intellectual activities. The evidence advanced has been of three sorts: anatomical, experimental, and clinical.

Bolton (1903, 1909) has offered the most direct anatomical evidence. He examined histologically a number of cases of amentia and dementia and found a reduction in the thickness of the cerebral cortex and in the number of well-developed neurons (particularly in the pyramidal layers) in all. These deviations from the normal condition were most evident in the prefrontal region and led him to conclude:

> The great anterior center of association, lying in the prefrontal region, is underdeveloped on the one hand in all grades of mental deficiency, and on the other undergoes primary atrophy *pari passu* with the development of dementia; it is therefore the region of the cerebrum which is concerned with the highest co-ordinating and associational processes of the mind.

The material presented by Bolton establishes the lesser development or degeneration of the cortex in cases of defective intelligence, but the evidence for the special importance of the frontal lobes is by no means final. The number of cases studied was not large; and, although many measurements were made from each brain examined, the results are not presented in such a way as to establish their statistical validity. Only the prefrontal and the "visuo-psychic" and "visuo-sensory" areas were compared. Moreover, exact measurements of the depth of cortical laminations are exceedingly difficult; and, owing to the indefinite boundaries of the layers, the personal equation of the investigator must enter in. Bolton himself states that measurements in the frontal region can be made more accurately than in other areas, and thus it is by no means clear that the closer correspondence between depth of laminations and degree of intelligence in the frontal than in the visual areas is a matter of fact rather than a result of the more accurate measurements possible in the frontal region.

Hammarberg (1895), examining a larger number of areas histologically, found the greatest cell deficiency in aments varying from area to area, not infrequently in the precentral and post-central gyri, and gave no intimation of a greater deficiency in the association areas than in other parts of the cortex.

The experimental work bearing upon the localization of intelligence has been most adequately summarized by Bianchi (1922). He reviews the anatomical and experimental evidence and develops a theory of hierarchies of correlating centers, of which the frontal lobes form the highest level. To the parietal and temporal association areas he assigns a subordinate rôle, which nevertheless is of great importance:

> The temporal lobe contributes to the formation and manifestation of the intellect not only by means of the simple auditory images, which represent one of the modes by which the world is revealed to us, but especially by means of language. It is by means of language that we are enabled to recompose in our minds our world of cognitions, along with the ever-growing and manifold network of our social relations, which offer an ever-increasing scope for the exercise and development of intellect.

Thus he recognizes the contribution of various parts of the cerebrum to intelligent acts but considers that their diverse functions are finally integrated through the activity of a specialized co-ordinating center. He asks,

> Does there exist a cerebral organ which has the faculty of using the mental products of the sensory areas of the cortex for the construction of mental syntheses more suited for the spiritualisation, and hence the cognition, of nature, an organ giving rise to reactions upon the world which, on the basis of individual and collective experience, permit a higher adaptation of the individual to his physical and social environment, an organ which renders possible the unfolding of a long process of logically connected thought?

To this question he gives emphatic affirmation, finding the highest level of integration in the frontal lobes. His conception of intelligence differs from that to which methods of mental testing have given rise; in some respects it corresponds more to the psychological definition of personality, but some of his discussions suggest that he ascribes to the frontal lobes more than this final synethesis, that he considers them of primary importance for all of the acts which we are accustomed to regard as intelligent.

Certainly the picture which he strives to deduce from his protocols of experiments is one of general dementia.

These experiments which he reports seem to me far from conclusive. True, they demonstrate a serious deterioration in dogs and monkeys after destruction of the frontal lobes, but there are no controls to show that lesions of equal extent in other parts of the cortex are not attended by an equal deterioration. He reports experiments on five dogs and eight monkeys. In some of the dogs he injured other areas than the frontal without finding deterioration, but these lesions were unilateral and of no great extent. In the monkeys he reports no lesions outside of the frontal field. Without an equivalent series of cases with lesions of equal extent in other regions than the frontal, the experiments prove nothing concerning the localization of intelligence.

The observations of Franz (1902, 1907) upon the loss of habits following destruction of the frontal lobes show a localization of habits within this area; but, since his animals relearned the problems without significant retardation, the results are directly opposed to those of Bianchi and indicate that the animals are not demented after destruction of the frontal lobes.

The first clinical study in which the precaution of comparing systematically the symptoms of frontal-lobe injury with those of lesions in other parts of the cerebrum is that of Feuchtwanger (1923), who compared two hundred cases of frontal lesion with an equal number of cases with injuries in other regions. He found no characteristic defects of intellect in the frontal cases. There were emotional and temperamental changes, but intelligence was affected only in so far as it seems to be conditioned by emotional factors. He concludes, "Certainly we must say that the intellect and the functions implying it, perception, memory, thinking, the flow of movements and of skilled acts, are not specifically disturbed." The character changes noted may fit in with Bianchi's conception of intelligence, which is none too clearly defined, but are certainly distinct from the sort of thing which we seek to measure by intelligence tests.

Many of the recent studies upon symptoms arising from injuries restricted to sensory or "sensoripsychic" areas suggest that disturbances of function which have previously been classed as purely sensory actually resemble disorders of intellect rather than a lowered sensory efficiency (e.g., the series of cases reviewed by Klüver, 1927). Such observations suggest that the intellectual achievements of single sensory areas are not slight and that the defects resulting from injuries to the areas need not be fundamentally different in kind from certain aspects of what we call "general dementia."

From the lack of reliable quantitative measurements of intelligence, the inadequacy of the histological study of the brain in many instances, and the failure to take into account the absolute magnitude of the injuries in the frontal and other regions, the existing literature upon the functions of the association areas is of no great value for the problem of intelligence. It certainly fails to establish that these areas are of any more importance for intelligent behavior than are any other portions of the cerebral cortex. The doctrine of hierarchies of organization within the central nervous system with a supreme organizing center as the agent for the most elaborate integrations, a seat of the higher intellectual faculties, is not established, however useful it may have been as an aid to the schematic representation of neural function.

This brief sketch of psychological and neurological theories of intelligence will serve to show the diversity of opinions still held concerning the nature and mechanism of the function and will help to define our problem when we seek to analyze the brain processes which are essential to intelligent activity. The most fundamental difference among the theories is with respect to the unity of intelligence. By one group it is regarded as an aggregate of the separate efficiencies of specialized faculties (Munk, Monakow, Thorndike); by the other, as a unitary function which transcends the special capacities and adds to or subtracts from their several efficiencies (Hitzig, Bianchi, Spearman). The adherents of the latter view are again divided with respect to the mechanisms involved. The extreme localizationists consider that intelligence consists of a special manner of integrating the products of the sensory fields, as in the operation of Hitzig's center for abstract thinking. A more moderate view is embodied in theories, like that of Bianchi, that the association centers add only a final stage of integration to the connections already established within the functionally lower levels of the cortex; being thus true co-ordinating centers rather than regions for special kinds of elaboration. Finally there are the doctrines of Goltz and Loeb, concurred in to some extent by Spearman's theory of nervous energy, maintaining that intelligence is a dynamic function of the whole cortex acting as a unit rather than by the summation of qualitatively diverse functions. None of the theories seems clearly established by the existing evidence. On the whole the psychological evidence seems to favor the existence of some single variable like Spearman's g, in addition to special abilities; but whether this represents the activity of a special co-ordinating center, the general physiological level of efficiency of the whole brain, or some wholly unknown mechanism, like Loeb's capacity for resonance, is still an open question.

The whole problem is in confusion. It is uncertain whether we are justified in dealing with intelligence as a single function, as an algebraic sum of all functions, or as the sum of a few selected ones. There is further involved the problem of valuation. So long as we judge intelligence in terms of the effectiveness of integration (success in life or school, for example), we are unlikely to discover any simple physiological correlate. On the other hand, attempts to formulate it in terms of the completeness or complexity of integration are baffled by the lack of any objective measure of these attributes. The only hope of solution of such difficulties seems to lie in an exhaustive study of the interdependence of various specific activities of the organism. Spearman's general factor and Thorndike's "Intellect CAVD" present results of a satisfactory method, but both must be carried much farther before definite correspondences to physiological variates can be revealed.

The concept of intelligence is becoming essentially a statistical one; it is the correlation between certain of the activities of the organism which are closely related among themselves and relatively independent of other activities. Among such groupings of activities, what correlatives constitute intelligence, as opposed to other capacities? There is no accepted statement which really defines the concept. Thorndike suggests correlation with the "trait which sensible people, psychologists, and teachers rate as intellect." Spearman's g is the common factor in the results of intelligence tests and so, likewise, appeals ultimately to intuitive recognition of the function. These approaches thus leave us no better off in understanding the nature of intelligence, yet they do establish beyond question the existence of some variable factor which in part determines the individual's effectiveness in a variety of activities. That this is primarily a function of the activity of nervous tissue and that its nature is thus finally to be stated in terms of the mechanisms of the brain seems certain.

THE PROBLEM OF INTELLIGENCE IN EXPERIMENTS WITH ANIMALS

The complexities of human behavior in test situations have given little indication of the nature of the brain mechanisms. It is possible that a more direct attack upon the latter may reveal more of the nature of the general factor. Such a direct approach can be made only through experimental studies with animals, and the difficulties of definition and interpretation are not lessened when we turn to the field of comparative psychology. We are confronted with the problem of identifying the behavior of our animal subjects with those aspects of human behavior which we call "intelligent"; and this is especially difficult if the work is with animals low in the evolutionary scale, having restricted sensorimotor capacities and a limited range of activities.

Formulations of the problem in the past have been quite arbitrary. The criteria of intelligence most frequently used have been either the capacity to learn or the appearance of insight. Loeb (1902) practically identified associative memory with intelligence, and in this followed the lead of earlier physiologists and has been followed in turn by many students of animal behavior. Yerkes (1927) and Köhler (1921), on the other hand, have stressed the rôle of insight and have distinguished intelligence rather sharply from mechanical learning.

Neither of these approaches to the problem seems altogether satisfactory. There are some instances of associative memory, such as the conditioned glandular reflexes, which do not conform to our intuitional judgments of intelligence and which would be classified as unintelligent by the majority of students. Certainly, to say that, because the amoeba can form a simple association (Mast and Pusch, 1918), it exhibits a low form of intelligence helps us not at all to understand either the mechanism of intelligence in man or the "mind of amoeba." We cannot now draw any satisfactory line between intelligent and unintelligent associative memory, and the term used without restriction includes too much. On the other hand, those who define intelligence in terms of insight tend to limit the latter concept too sharply. The essence of insight, by the definition of the Gestalt school, is responsiveness to configurations, that is, in a more behavioristic terminology, responsiveness to the relationships of the physical elements of the stimulating situation rather than to the isolated elements. This type of behavior is not restricted to the execution of "intelligent" tasks. The definition applies as well to some of the tropistic responses of insects (e.g., where the direction of orientation is determined by the *relative* intensity of two sources of light) as to the behavior of the chimpanzee.

There is thus little more hope of finding a satisfactory formulation of animal intelligence than of human, and we must fall back upon the same method of analysis which seems to promise an empirical solution of the human problem, the determination of intercorrelations among specific activities. The one advantage of the infrahuman subjects lies in the fact that we may control directly some of the nervous functions and test their correlation with the traits of behavior. Can we find in animals a constellation of activities, correlating among themselves, having some of the attributes of human intelligence, and capable of modification through experimental control of nervous functions? If so, there is a chance for insight into the nature of the variable which is responsible for the correlations, for a neurological account of intelligence.

OBJECT OF THE PRESENT EXPERIMENTS

The experiments to be reported are an attempt to sample the activities of the rat, to determine the correlations among them, and to test the influence of certain neurological variables upon them. The limited number of tests and of subjects tested is an unavoidable defect of the study. The selection of tests may be more justly criticized. They all deal with some aspect of the learning process, and its relation to the problem of intelligence is not yet clearly established.

The great majority of recent discussions of learning in animals have developed under the influence of the doctrine of random activities and the elimination of useless movements. Habits are conceived as successions of movements, isolated save for simple associations with the preceding and subsequent links of the chain, as simple concatenations of conditioned reflexes. Such a view precludes any attempt to relate the findings from studies of animal learning with human insight or reactions to relations. Capacity to memorize has shown but low correlations with intelligence, measured by other criteria; and, to the extent that our studies of learning in animals are what they have purported to be, measures of mnemonic capacity, they are irrelevant to the problem of intelligence.

I began the study of cerebral function with a definite bias toward such an interpretation of the learning problem. The original program of research looked toward the tracing of conditioned-reflex arcs through the cortex, as the spinal paths of simple reflexes seemed to have been traced through the cord. The experimental findings have never fitted into such a scheme. Rather, they have emphasized the unitary character of every habit, the impossibility of stating any learning as a concatenation of reflexes, and the participation of large masses of nervous tissue in the functions rather than the development of restricted conduction-paths.

Likewise, attempts to analyze the maze and problem-box habits in terms of adequate stimulus and conditioned-reflex response have indicated that the problem is far from solved by the simple mechanical theories of learning. Random activity, association, and retention constitute only a small part of the totality of processes underlying the formation of such habits, and even with the rat in the maze there is more than a little indicaton that direct adaptive reactions and some process of generalization are of fundamental importance for the learning process. Evidence in support of this statement will be presented later. For the present I wish merely to emphasize that the interpretation of learning in animals as a simple conditioning is by no means established.

The primary requirements for the tests were that they be capable of giving fairly accurate quantitative results and that some objective estimate of their difficulty or complexity be possible. Of the available techniques, the learning tests alone could qualify. The results obtained seem to have justified their selection.

CHAPTER II

GENERAL METHODS

The experiments to be reported include training of rats in a variety of problems either before or after destruction of parts of the cerebral cortex, with retention tests to determine the influence of lesions upon previously formed habits or upon retention of habits formed after injury. They differ in details of training methods, controls, and the like, but involve many common points and problems of technique.

SURGICAL AND ANATOMICAL METHODS

All operations were performed under deep ether anesthesia with aseptic precautions. Except in one case, the linear lesions of No. 1, which were made with a knife, a thermocautery was used to destroy the cortex. Lesions involving more than 50 per cent of the cortex usually required two successive operations with an intervening period for recovery from shock. Postoperative retention tests were begun 10 days after operation. This interval was ample for recovery from all signs of operative shock or depression, and in no case was it necessary to prolong the period because of inactivity or lack of vigor of the animals. Tests which I have reported in other studies (Lashley, 1927) make it clear that the question of general surgical shock is adequately controlled by this interval. In experiments on initial learning after very extensive injuries to the cortex it was sometimes necessary to wait for a longer interval before beginning training, but this was true only in the cases which later proved to have extensive subcortical lesions.

At necropsy the position and extent of the superficial lesions were determined from the freshly removed brain and laid off on diagrams of the brain with proportional dividers. The actual lesions are always more extensive than indicated by the appearance of the surface of the brain, so that these preliminary determinations are of value only as a check upon the later reconstruction from sections. The brains were fixed, sectioned, and stained with carbol thionin. The use of a general cell stain permits a more accurate delimitation of the extent of cell destruction than do the methods of demonstrating degeneration. The mass of material precludes any detailed study of fiber degeneration in individual cases, and the uncertainty of techniques for demonstrating degeneration of the finer fibers at long intervals after injury would render such studies of less value for our present purpose than the gross determination of cortical destruction.

Serial sections at intervals of $\frac{1}{4}$ millimeter were sketched under camera lucida. The limits of the lesions were determined under higher magnification and filled in free-hand on the sketches by reference to selected landmarks. The dimensions of the lesions were transferred to corresponding levels on the printed diagrams, shown in the plates, and the points so determined connected by the best fitting line. These outlines were compared with the original diagrams made at necropsy, and in case of significant difference the reconstruction was repeated. The areas of these lesions were finally measured from the diagrams with a planimeter and expressed as percentage of the total surface area.

Measurements from the diagrams involve a certain error due to overlapping of the dorsal and lateral views and to perspective. This was partially corrected by omitting from the measurement of the diagrams of the lateral surfaces all parts of the lesion lying above the level of the corpus callosum. Measurements taken directly from the perimeters of the sections of a typical brain give almost exactly the same figures as those obtained from the diagram; but where the brains were distorted during fixation, some additional error is introduced.

The measurements are of actual destruction of the cortex. In most cases all of the underlying fibers were destroyed; but no attempt has been made to deal with areas rendered non-functional by section of their association or projection tracts, since our knowledge of these is too slight to serve as a basis for an estimate of the areas supplied by given tracts in the external capsule. The lesions represented are therefore minimal, and considerably larger areas than are indicated in the diagrams were certainly involved in some cases. In quantitative studies such as these, the impossibility of exact delimitation of the lesions reduces the reliability of the results; yet this fact may be discounted to some extent in that consistent quantitative relationships have been demonstrated in spite of it, both in the present studies and in the previous study of brightness discrimination (Lashley, 1927). Moreover, it is questionable whether we should be justified in recording areas as non-functional because of partial section of their connections, for there is some evidence that the function of an area may be unimpaired by the section of a considerable portion of its association fibers.

When, as in the present experiments, variations both in the position and in the extent of lesions seem to influence the symptoms in a similar manner and to an unknown extent, the interpretation of the data becomes very difficult. The present experiments must be regarded only as a crude preliminary survey of the problems.

In attempts to destroy large areas of the cortex it is impossible to avoid occasional injuries to the deep-lying structures—striatum, hippocampus, fornix, septum, and thalamus. Such injuries have been carefully analyzed and taken into account in the discussions of different experiments.

GRAPHIC AND STATISTICAL METHODS

The number of cases reported is too large for the inclusion of individual protocols, but the more important data are summarized in plates and tables. Diagrams of the lesions in individual cases are included in the plates, arranged for each experiment in the order of magnitude of the lesions, without regard to the areas involved. When necessary, composite diagrams summarizing the lesions in a number of cases are given. These have been constructed by superimposing the diagrams for the separate cases and blocking in either the areas common to all or the total area covered by all cases under consideration.

The best method of handling the quantitative data is open to question. Of the three criteria of learning used in these experiments—total time, total trials, or total errors preceding the attainment of an arbitrary number of errorless trials—time is probably the least reliable. This has been shown by Tolman (1924) in maze studies with normal animals and is particularly true for animals with extensive brain lesions, which may show a slowing of movement without corresponding inaccuracy of maze-running. A single error made after a series of perfect runs may disproportionately increase the total number of trials, so that, on the whole, errors seem the most reliable of the three criteria. However, records are given separately for the three, and in most cases the constants have been computed separately and are given for all. When it is only a question of the influence of some sub-division of the data upon an average or correlation, only the constants for errors have been computed. The trend of the results shown by all of the criteria is the same.

It is sometimes desirable to express the records of time, errors, and trials as a single figure. This has been done for the operated groups by determining the value of each constant as a percentage of the corresponding average for normal animals and then taking the average of these percentages as a combined expression of the three criteria.

Individual variations, both in extent of lesion and in training records, deviate from the curve of normal distribution; so in computing correlations it has seemed best to use the rank-difference method, in preference to the product-moment, by the formula

$$p = 1 - \frac{6\Sigma d^2}{n(n^2 - 1)} .$$

Probable errors of p were computed by the formula

$$\text{P.E.}_p = \frac{1 - p^2}{\sqrt{n}} 0.7063 .$$

In dealing with the records of animals under different conditions, as in preliminary and postoperative retention tests, we may use as a standard for comparison either the individual records or the averages of a group. In tests of amnesia following operation, where it is a question of deciding whether or not each individual has lost the habit, the choice of a method is important.

Since there is no correlation between records for initial learning and records for preliminary retention tests, I have judged that differences in the records of normal animals are largely due to chance and are not characteristic of the individuals. The comparisons of individual postoperative records have therefore been made with the group averages for the records of preliminary training.

RELIABILITY OF THE METHODS

The reliability of the methods of measuring the lesions has already been considered. The actual measurements of cerebral destruction are sufficiently accurate, but the secondary involvement of other regions through injury to projection tracts or association fibers or through the action of diaschisis is an unknown quantity. It seems just to assume, however, that these secondary involvements are either proportional to the total measurable extent of cortical destruction or not of a character such as to produce a spurious correlation between measurable extent of injury and efficiency of performance.

Hunter (1922), Heron (1922, 1924), Tolman (1924), and Hunter and Randolph (1924) have cast some doubt upon the validity of our present methods of measuring learning in animals. Their studies have dealt with groups of normal adult animals which probably include a relatively small range of variation and which show insignificant correlation between the various constants used to measure individual differences.

Stone and Nyswander (1927), using different criteria of reliability, have shown that within any limited part of the training the behavior of the animals is quite consistent. This indicates that the criteria used in studies of maze learning do differentiate the animals reliably with respect to some function, although it is not clear whether this is the capacity to learn or some other character such as timidity or degree of motivation.

To test the reliability of Maze III, I have followed the method suggested by Hunter of correlating the records of the first 10 trials with the records for complete learning. To avoid overlapping of the data and consequent spurious correlation, the average time per trial and the average errors per trial for the first 10 trials of training were correlated with the total number of trials required to reach the criterion of learning. The measures correlated are thus mutually exclusive. These constants for the maze have been computed for the initial learning of a group of 59 normal animals, for initial learning of a group of 37 animals with cerebral lesions, and for retention tests of 59 animals after cerebral injury. The constants for the three groups are the following:

	CORRELATIONS, TOTAL TRIALS WITH TIME AND ERROR RECORDS OF FIRST TEN TRIALS	
	Time	Errors
Learning, normal animals.......	0.09±0.09	0.06±0.09
Learning, after operation.......	0.18±0.11	0.62±0.08
Retention after operation.......	0.76±0.04	0.79±0.04

The intercorrelations between two of the mazes used in the experiments have been computed for initial learning of normal animals and of animals after cerebral injuries. They are:

	CORRELATION, MAZES III WITH IV		
	Time	Errors	Trials
Normal animals.........	−0.09±0.18	−0.36±0.16	−0.38±0.15
Operated animals.......	0.55±0.09	0.67±0.07	0.68±0.07

For normal animals, the correlations of the first 10 trials with total trials indicate that differences found between individuals are not reliable. The correlations between Mazes III and IV are negative and larger, but not significantly greater than their probable errors. There is sufficient difference in the character of the two mazes to suggest that the negative correlation for normal animals may not be spurious, although its possible significance is not clear.

For the operated animals, the correlations are all much higher and are significantly greater than their probable errors. These results indicate that, although the maze methods are inadequate to reveal the slight variations within a normal adult population, they do form an adequate measure of the enormously greater differences within a group of animals having extensive injuries to the cerebrum.

There are serious objections to the foregoing methods of measuring the reliability of tests. The use of intercorrelations of the results of training upon different problems involves the assumption that learning ability is a unitary function which should be revealed by any reliable measure—an assumption which is totally unjustified by the experimental literature on human or animal learning. The lack of a correlation between two reliable but dissimilar learning problems forms a valid objection to any conclusion concerning learning capacity in general, but it does not necessarily give an index of the adequacy of the measures to reveal individual differences in ability to learn either problem.

Failure to find a high correlation between the data on the first 10 trials of training and some arbitrary measure of complete learning is also not a conclusive argument against the validity of the latter, since a correlation between a reliable and an entirely unreliable measure need not be higher than between two unreliable ones. Where there is no other variable which can be measured more reliably, we cannot choose between different parts of the learning curve and must discard all measures as untrustworthy. But where some additional and measurable variable is introduced, it is possible to evaluate the measures of learning by their closeness of correspondence to this variable, provided it is not of such a character as directly to affect the measures themselves.

Thus a comparison of the extent of injuries within the occipital areas of the rat with the amount of practice required for relearning the habit of brightness discrimination revealed correlations of the order 0.72 by several criteria of learning and by all methods of subdividing the data which did not result in reduction of the range of variation. This shows that the retention tests were a fairly valid measure of the amount of brain injury, whether or not they actually measured retention.

In the present experiments, Table XI (page 73) shows the relation between the extent of brain injury and the rate of initial learning of four different mazes. The table includes five sets of permutations, each of six figures. Among these thirty elements of the permutations there are only two inversions of the order from least to greatest. The probability of such a correspondence occurring by chance is less than one to fifty billions.

These considerations seem to me to form a valid argument against the extension of conclusions concerning the reliability of the maze, based upon studies of normal animals only, to any experiments in which other variables are introduced. Thus, although the scores made in the initial stages of practice do not correlate highly with the final measures of learning,[1] the consistency of the results and the closeness of correspondence between the records for final learning and the extent of brain injury indicate that, for the conditions of the experiment, Maze III and the Yerkes discrimination box provide an adequate measure of some function which is affected by brain injuries. They give no indication of the fineness of this measure, but this is a common defect of all methods of evaluating tests.

Whether we are dealing with learning ability in general, with a learning capacity specific for the problems in which the animals were trained, or with some other function than that of learning is not revealed by the correlation alone. It must be decided on the basis of other data; intercorrelations between results with different problems, analysis of the behavior essential for the performance of the habits, and the like.

DIFFICULTIES OF INTERPRETATION IN STUDIES OF BRAIN INJURIES

In analysis of the symptoms of brain injury it seems that we must take into account a number of variables which, because of practical difficulties of technique, are almost impossible of independent control. They enormously complicate the problem; yet, until we have some means of evaluating them severally, we

---

[1] I am not inclined to use any criterion of maze learning which does not involve the attainment of a fairly stable errorless performance. Our interest is primarily in the acquisition of the maze pattern, and only errorless trials give certain evidence for this. Improvement in time or reduction in errors may indicate that the pattern is being learned but in the earlier stages of training is probably indicative of nothing more than adaptation to a strange situation.

can form no true conception of the cerebral mechanisms. The variables which may be clearly recognized in a series of cases seem to be:

1. *Individual variation in localization.*—Anatomical studies of the area striata have shown that the cortical fields delimited by cell structure vary considerably from one individual to another. Adequate data of this sort are available only for this area, and even here give only the fact of variation without determination of the limits of the range or the distribution of variates. By physiological methods also, indication of this variability is obtained. Observations here are unambiguous only for the motor area, but the results of Franz (1915) show clearly that even in the two hemispheres of the same animal the arrangement of excitable points differs greatly. Whether this variability is primarily the result of anatomical differences or whether it indicates that functional organization is in some measure independent of structure is uncertain. My observations on temporal variation in the function of the motor area (Lashley, 1923) suggest that both anatomical variation and changes in physiological organization may be effective agents in producing the appearance of functional variability.

2. *Specific shock or diaschisis effects.*—Monakow (1914) has emphasized the rôle played in the production of recoverable symptoms by temporary loss of function in one center as a result of destruction of another. The conception is doubtless a valuable one for the understanding of many cases of spontaneous recovery, but its practical application is complicated by the frequent difficulty in distinguishing between spontaneous recovery and recovery as a result of re-education. We have as yet no understanding of the manner in which the diaschisis effect is produced or any way of predicting the most probable shock effects from injury to any particular locus.

3. *Vicarious function.*—Improvement through re-education has been interpreted as the assumption of the functions of injured parts by others which have escaped injury. There is much incorrect speculation in the older literature concerning the parts functioning vicariously, as the assumption that the precentral

gyrus of one side can assume the functions of that of the other; but there is no certain evidence that the reacquired functions are carried out vicariously by any specific loci. Attempts to discover such loci have been in almost all cases fruitless (Lashley, 1922) and point rather to a reorganization of the entire neural mass than to an action of specific areas. The spontaneous and re-educative improvements after cerebral lesions make it exceedingly difficult to draw final conclusions from any syndrome concerning cerebral function, since a gradual improvement may be ascribed to recovery from shock, even though it occurs during a post-operative retraining.

4. *Equipotentiality of parts.*—The term "equipotentiality" I have used to designate the apparent capacity of any intact part of a functional area to carry out, with or without reduction in efficiency, the functions which are lost by destruction of the whole. This capacity varies from one area to another and with the character of the functions involved. It probably holds only for the association areas and for functions more complex than simple sensitivity or motor co-ordination.

5. *Mass function.*—I have already given evidence (1927), which is augmented in the present study, that the equipotentiality is not absolute but is subject to a law of mass action whereby the efficiency of performance of an entire complex function may be reduced in proportion to the extent of brain injury within an area whose parts are not more specialized for one component of the function than for another.

6. *Disturbances of the equilibrium within functional systems.*—There is a considerable mass of evidence which suggests that some symptoms, particularly in the class of motor inco-ordinations, may result from disturbances in the functional equilibrium between centers, although no tissue essential to the performance of the disturbed activities is directly involved in the lesion. Thus unilateral lesions to the corpus striatum or to the cerebellum may produce marked disturbances of co-ordination although bilaterally symmetrical lesions involving the same structures produce but slight effects.

In evaluating any symptoms following cerebral lesion we must consider the possible intervention of each of these factors. In some cases the differentiation is relatively easy, as in ruling out diaschisis as an element in the production of a permanent defect of learning ability, but this is rather an exceptional instance. Wherever possible, I have attempted to distinguish the rôle of such different factors, but in many cases this must await the accumulation of far more evidence.

CHAPTER III

THE INFLUENCE OF CEREBRAL LESIONS UPON THE CAPACITY TO LEARN

In 1918 I reported a first attempt to determine the influence of the extent of lesions to the cerebrum upon the rat's ability to form a motor habit. For the purpose the double-platform box was used (Fig. 1). This is a problem box provided with a door

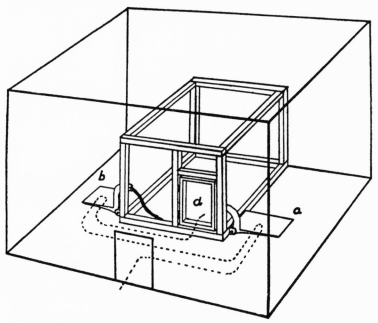

FIG. 1.—The double-platform box used in earlier studies. The door (d) is opened when the platforms (a, b) are successively pressed down.

which is opened by successively pressing down in predetermined order two platforms attached to opposite sides of the box. Nineteen animals were trained in this habit after cerebral lesions involving from 14 to 50 per cent of the cortex. The average amount of destruction was 28.4 per cent. The operated animals required only 75 per cent as much practice as normal animals learning under the same conditions. Correction for the effects of motor disturbance in the operated cases indicated that the cerebral destruction produced no significant effect upon the learning ability for this habit. The rank-order correlation between extent of lesion and amount of practice for the animals in this series is $p=0.24\pm0.15$. Corrected for cases with motor disturbance, there remains no significant difference in learning ability between animals with slight and animals with extensive brain injuries.

In a more recent study (1926) I reported experiments on the influence of lesions within the area striata upon the animal's ability to form a simple visual habit. Forty-eight animals were trained in brightness discrimination after cerebral lesions in the occipital region ranging from 3.5 to 43.9 per cent of the total area of the neopallium. The operated animals required 94 per cent as much practice as normal animals trained under similar conditions. In relation to its probable error this difference is not significant. The correlation between extent of lesion and amount of practice required for learning in this series was $p=0.11\pm0.14$. These figures justified the conclusion that the capacity to learn the habit of brightness discrimination is unaffected by any injury to the occipital half of the cerebrum, even including the entire area striata of both hemispheres.

Further data on these two problems indicated that when normal animals which had learned the habits were subjected to cerebral lesion in restricted areas, the habits were lost (Hunter, 1926; Lashley, 1927), in which case they could be reacquired by an amount of practice not exceeding the range for normal animals.

In contrast to this, loss of the maze habit following cerebral lesions proved to be attended by great difficulty in relearning, sometimes by total inability to reacquire the habit. This opened a new method of attack upon the problem of deterioration after brain injury and called for a more extensive investigation of the whole question.

PROBLEMS AND SPECIAL METHODS

In planning the experiments the following questions seemed most pressing:

1. Are there situations for the rat in which a deterioration of learning ability after brain injury can be demonstrated, as well as those, like the double-platform box, in which no defect appears? If so, what determines the involvement or non-involvement of the capacity to acquire each particular activity? To test this, it was desirable to sample as many different activities as possible; and in preliminary experiments the multiple choice method of Yerkes (1916), the perseverance reaction of Hamilton (1916), the alternation problem of Carr (1917), a variety of latch boxes, pattern vision, and several tests of direct adaptation to changes in the maze were tried out, in addition to the problems finally selected.

2. Is the deterioration following cerebral lesion temporary or permanent? To test this it was necessary, when reduced learning ability had been demonstrated for one type of problem, to train upon another similar problem at a later date, allowing at least a sufficient interval for complete recovery from any shock or diaschisis effect.

3. What is the influence of the locus of injury upon the capacity to learn different types of problems? This necessitates testing the effects of lesions in all possible parts of the cortex upon the learning of a variey of problems.

4. What is the effect of the magnitude of the lesion upon various types of learning? This requires lesions of different magnitude in each of the areas studied.

5. What is the relation between the sensory components of the problem, the locus of injury, and the degree of deterioration? To test this it was desirable to present problems offering different and controllable sensory cues.

6. What is the relation between the complexity of the habit and the degree of retardation after brain injury? To test this it was desirable to include several problems having the same sensorimotor basis and differing in the number of identical components included in each. Mazes most nearly meet this requirement but present the difficulty that one must either vary the pattern considerably, and so introduce other factors than the re-

duplication of parts, or risk obscuring results by permitting a large amount of transfer from one to another.

7. Is the capacity to remember affected in the same way as the capacity to learn? This calls for retention tests for the different types of situations studied.

8. When deterioration exists, is it due to sensory defect, to reduced motor control, to lowered efficiency of the mechanism of fixation, to a general functioning at a lower level of complexity, or what not? These questions demand a variety of tests and controls beyond immediate experimental possibility. They determined the inclusion of two problems, reversal of Maze I and the incline box, as tests of plasticity and of kinaesthesis.

It was desirable to observe the behavior of the same animals in a variety of situations, since only so could the effects of the same lesions in different situations be tested. This limited the number of problems which could be used to the capacity of the most retarded cases and made it necessary to discard the majority of the problem situations which were included in the preliminary tests. Most of these either required too great time for learning or failed to provide a clear-cut objective criterion of learning.

Ten problems were finally selected for study. To test the influence of complexity of problem on degree of deterioration three mazes were used; and for the permanence of defect, a fourth. For diversity of sensory components the brightness habit and the incline box were included. Retention tests for two mazes and the brightness habit, and a test for the ease of substituting one habit for another, completed the series. A detailed description of the problems follows.

1. *Maze III.*—This is a maze with eight culs-de-sac requiring alternate right and left turns in the true path (Fig. 2). It is arranged for automatic recording of errors. The animals were given 5 trials per day until 10 consecutive errorless trials were obtained. Time consumed and errors per trial were recorded. In case learning was much retarded, training was discontinued after 150 trials, which is more than seven times the average requirement of normal animals, and almost twice the upper range of normal cases.

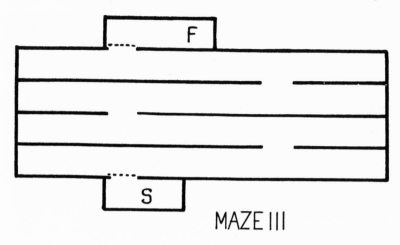

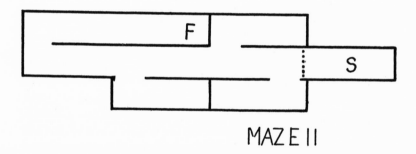

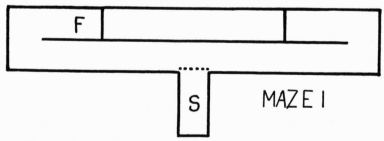

Fig. 2.—Ground plans of the inclosed mazes used in the present study. S, starting compartments; F, food compartments. The broken lines represent trap-doors which prevent return to the starting-box. Scale, 1 inch equals 1 foot.

2. *Maze II.*—This is a relatively simple maze having a straight path, with three culs-de-sac and the food compartment opening at the sides (Fig. 2). Training was continued at 5 trials per day until 10 consecutive errorless trials were obtained, or until 100 trials had been given. The latter is six times the average requirement for normal animals and three times the upper range of normal cases.

3. *Maze I.*—This is a simple T maze with one cul-de-sac to the right and food to the left (Fig. 2). With it, training was continued at 5 trials per day until 10 consecutive errorless trials were obtained, or until 60 trials had been given. The latter is four times the average requirement of normal animals and twice the upper limit of the range.

4. *Brightness discrimination.*—Animals were trained in a standard Yerkes box (Fig. 3) to choose the illuminated and avoid the darkened compartment. Training was continued at 10 trials per day until 30 consecutive errorless trials were obtained. No animal failed to reach this requirement.

5. *Retention of Maze III.*—Forty days after the completion of training on Maze III the animals were returned to it for tests of retention. These were given as were the original training tests and were continued to 10 consecutive errorless trials, or until 35 trials had been given. This is eighteen times the average requirement for relearning by normal animals and seven times the upper limit of their range.

6. *Retention of Maze I.*—On completion of retention tests for Maze III, a similar series was given for Maze I, with 5 trials per day to 10 consecutive errorless trials, or until 35 trials had been given. The latter is seven times the average requirements of normal animals and three times the upper limit of the normal range.

7. *Reversal of Maze I.*—After completion of the retention tests for Maze I the food was transferred to the cul-de-sac on the right and the animals trained to turn to the right and avoid the former correct path. Training was continued at 5 trials per day to 10 consecutive errorless trials, or until 50 trials had been given. The latter is four times the average requirement of nor-

mal animals and nearly three times the upper limit of their range.

8. *Retention of brightness discrimination.*—Retraining tests were given in the discrimination box until 30 consecutive errorless trials were obtained.

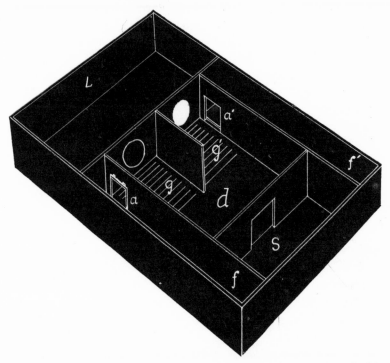

FIG. 3.—Box used for training in brightness discrimination. The animal is started at *S* and passes to *d*, where a choice of an illuminated and dark alley is offered. These lead across electric grills (*g, g'*) through trapdoors of light celluloid (*a, a'*) to the food compartments (*f, f'*). In training, the door on the dark side is locked and the grill charged. The illumination is shifted irregularly from side to side by a movable screen in the light-box (*L*). In use the entire box is covered except for an observation hood above *d*.

9. *Maze IV.*—This maze has the general plan of Maze III, reversed (Fig. 4), but requires the animal to run along the edges of vertically placed boards, $\frac{3}{16}$ inch in width, after the method devised by Miles (1927). Animals were given 5 trials per day to 10 consecutive errorless trials, or until 60 trials had been giv-

en. The latter is nine times the average requirement of normal animals and three times the upper limit of their range.

10. *Incline box.*—As a test of the possible loss of somesthetic sensitivity some of the more deteriorated of the operated cases were trained in a problem box which required discrimination of the direction of slope of an inclined surface. The problem box is of essentially the same form as Maze I, arranged so that it

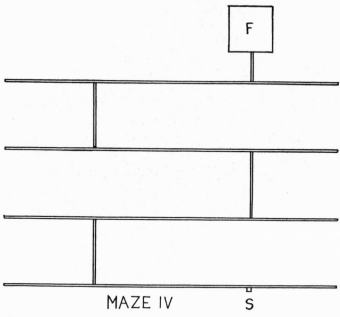

Fig. 4.—Ground plan of open maze. This was constructed of $\frac{3}{16}$-inch boards set on edge and supported 2 feet above the floor. *S*, starting-point; *F*, feeding-platform.

may be tilted laterally at an angle of $12\frac{1}{2}°$ with either end elevated above the other. The box is inclosed, light-tight, and the alleys wired with punishment grills and with signal contacts which record the animal's position. The animals were trained to turn up the incline on leaving the starting-compartment. Ten trials per day were given until 30 consecutive errorless trials were obtained.

The animals were trained successively in these problems in the order in which they are listed above. In the majority of cases training in each problem was begun immediately upon the completion of the tests with the preceding problem, but with some of the cases having more extensive lesions, which lose weight under the conditions of training, it was necessary to introduce a rest period of a week or more between problems.

Hunger was used as the incentive in all the mazes; a combination of hunger and electric shocks in the discrimination habits.

Fifty animals were subjected to cerebral lesion and started on the series of problems at an interval of from 10 to 30 days after operation, depending upon the rate of recovery from operation. Thirteen were discarded because of illness in the early stages of training or because of evidence of infection of the brain tissue at necropsy. Others died during the course of the experiment so that only 21 completed the series of problems. In addition 22 normal animals were started in the series of problems under similar training conditions. Six of these died during an epidemic of dysentery before completion of the series.

When symptoms of illness developed in any animal, training was discontinued immediately, and his record for the problem last completed was discarded, as a control of the effect of earlier undetected illness. Thus in Table I the animals recorded as dead after learning Maze III had completed Maze II, and so on.

The complete records for the operated animals are given in Table I and diagrams of the lesions in Plates I–IV, Figs. 1–37. In this series are included six animals which had been trained in brightness discrimination before operation and which therefore lack data on this problem. There is no indication of any influence of their previous training upon their records in this experiment. The records of the normal controls are given in Table II. Upon the data included in these two tables the following analyses are based.

DETERIORATION OF OPERATED ANIMALS SHOWN BY
MASSED RECORDS

We shall first consider the average effects of cerebral lesions, disregarding locus and magnitude; then examine more closely

TABLE I

INDIVIDUAL RECORDS OF LEARNING OR RETENTION IN 10 PROBLEMS, MADE BY ANIMALS AFTER CEREBRAL LESIONS. THE PERCENTAGE OF THE TOTAL NEOPALLIUM DESTROYED IS GIVEN AT THE LEFT. DIAGRAMS ILLUSTRATING THE LESIONS ARE GIVEN UNDER CORRESPONDING NUMBERS IN PLATES I–IV. TOTAL TIME SPENT IN PRACTICE, TOTAL ERRORS DURING TRAINING, AND TOTAL TRIALS PRECEDING THE 10 CONSECUTIVE ERRORLESS TRIALS (30 IN DISCRIMINATION EXPERIMENTS) ARE GIVEN FOR EACH ANIMAL

No.	Percentage of Destruction	Maze III			Maze II			Maze I		
		Time (in Seconds)	Errors	Trials	Time (in Seconds)	Errors	Trials	Time (in Seconds)	Errors	Trials
1...	1.5	111	5	3	20	2	3	74	9	28
2...	4.6	2,388	51	17	185	13	22	107	8	22
3...	6.0	8,842	126	47	340	24	19	0	0	0
4...	7.3	5,097	92	36	214	24	16	135	12	29
5...	7.9	2,131	112	62	134	10	10	79	5	16
6...	8.0	901	82	61	47	7	11	33	6	9
7...	8.4	2,357	43	31	45	4	4	23	1	1
8...	9.1	4,039	65	28	678	39	19	125	12	27
9...	11.2	4,321	165	51	390	28	26	94	7	13
10...	16.1	3,304	397	120	170	18	15	75	18	18
11...	16.4	1,972	338	77	236	33	50	36	4	5
12...	18.1	2,520	163	77	822	81	23	0	0	0
13...	22.6	5,108	332	54	410	54	33	108	27	36
14...	22.8	2,457	534	150 (23)*	157	34	42	67	20	1
15...	23.0	4,235	183	59	78	7	12	292	38	39
16...	23.9	13,567	621	86	506	51	100	471	61	60
17...	24.8	3,790	388	90	286	39	34	83	11	12
18...	24.9	1,202	206	59	281	20	22	136	17	17
19...	25.3	1,254	147	37	345	41	60	52	7	16
20...	26.9	11,931	752	150 (57)	1,280	273	100	756	91	60
21...	27.6	3,130	309	100	133	15	14	203	33	60
22...	27.9	5,207	444	150 (2)	253	30	18	0	0	0
23...	29.5	6,117	331	62	Died	......	......	......	......	......
24...	30.6	3,314	501	150 (0)	451	94	68	856	45	60
25...	32.0	3,128	193	60	392	31	43	277	30	51
26...	34.8	3,767	645	150 (0)	292	67	56	23	6	3
27...	39.8	12,909	617	73	291	59	86	172	52	60
28...	41.5	7,785	546	64	122	26	11	0	0	0
29...	44.8	14,121	809	106	541	90	91	156	23	22
30...	44.9	4,048	386	150 (0)	212	17	12	132	26	32
31...	53.3	4,622	682	150 (0)	Died	......	......	......	......	......
32...	54.9	9,561	761	111	1,129	64	82	11	1	1
33...	57.6	8,284	593	135	423	66	51	115	23	28
34...	65.3	17,142	2,287	150 (0)	1,955	470	60	1,000	18	13
35...	66.4	5,885	1,048	150 (0)	3,186	634	100	806	76	39
36...	69.5	15,479	1,423	150 (0)	Died	......	......	......	......	......
37...	81.2	18,224	1,330	150 (0)	667	75	40	22	2	4

* Figures in parentheses are errorless trials.

TABLE I—*Continued*

No.	Percentage of Destruction	Visual Discrimination		Maze III Retention			Maze I Retention		
		Errors	Trials	Time (in Seconds)	Errors	Trials	Time (in Seconds)	Errors	Trials
1....	1.5	21	60	4	2	1	65	7	15
2....	4.6	39	90	300	10	1	5	1	3
3....	6.0	18	70	Died	......	......	......	......	......
4....	7.3	40	140	674	61	6	80	8	16
5....	7.9	Died		......	......	......			
6....	8.0	46	130	135	9	18	0	0	0
7....	8.4	30	80	1,347	38	10	15	1	1
8....	9.1	Died		......	......	......			
9....	11.2	43	120	131	3	5	124	7	14
10....	16.1	33	160	......	......	......	89	6	8
11....	16.4	22	100	30	5	3	14	2	4
12....	18.1	10	30	4,018	433	35	163	2	2
13....	22.6	......	......	289	40	26	153	33	35
14....	22.8	38	100	431	51	35	0	0	0
15....	23.0	......	......	334	20	35	42	5	11
16....	23.9	......	......	303	39	35	194	35	35
17....	24.8	24	80	5,810	580	35	256	44	34
18....	24.9	......	......	402	48	35	7	1	2
19....	25.3	97	200	75	9	6	128	24	31
20....	26.9	48	170	1,423	152	35	F*	F	F
21....	27.6	......	......	306	41	35	117	23	35
22....	27.9	......	......	512	57	35	0	0	0
23....	29.5	......	......						
24....	30.6	19	80	1,067	127	35	246	50	35
25....	32.0	......	......	101	7	9	79	6	9
26....	34.8	11	70	991	102	35	167	21	23
27....	39.8	43	180	751	112	35	21	1	1
28....	41.5	23	50	3,799	190	10	51	3	4
29....	44.8	68	180	795	253	35	47	6	6
30....	44.9	45	140	466	93	35	0	0	0
31....	53.3	......	......						
32....	54.9	57	100	Died	......	......	......	......	......
33....	57.6	34	180	427	63	35	92	19	33
34....	65.3	64	120	Died	......	......	......	......	......
35 ...	66.4	108	230	927	270	35	0	0	0
36....	69.5	......	......	......			......		
37....	81.2	......	......	......			......		

* "F" indicates cases which failed through inactivity

TABLE I—*Continued*

No.	Percentage of Destruction	Maze I Reversal			Visual Discrimination Retention		Maze IV			Incline Box	
		Time (in Seconds)	Errors	Trials	Errors	Trials	Time (in Seconds)	Errors	Trials	Errors	Trials
1....	1.5	169	17	34	2	10	476	10	1	....	....
2....	4.6	52	5	6	0	0	4,868	26	14	6	20
3....	6.0	....	....	....	....	....	....	....	....	....	....
4....	7.3	101	12	33	0	0	2,808	87	17	....	....
5....	7.9	....	....	....	....	....	....	....	....	....	....
6....	8.0	65	15	29	3	10	3,113	17	7	14	40
7....	8.4	28	3	6	0	0	1,290	27	4	....	....
8....	9.1	....	....	....	....	....	....	....	....	....	....
9....	11.2	52	3	6	2	20	2,742	41	6	....	....
10....	16.1	351	29	37	9	50	10,792	255	60	....	....
11....	16.4	41	8	10	6	30	1,593	52	9	....	....
12....	18.1	289	24	38	2	10	5,865	339	60	....	....
13....	22.6	F*	F	F	....	....	4,666	481	60	17	40
14....	22.8	264	50	50	0	0	2,494	93	32	....	....
15....	23.0	69	5	7	....	....	4,355	228	60	....	....
16....	23.9	F	F	F	....	....	7,703	776	60	18	50
17....	24.8	269	24	18	1	10	F	F	F	....	....
18....	24.9	102	7	18	....	....	2,370	52	16	9	20
19....	25.3	53	10	16	2	20	1,858	89	22	....	....
20....	26.9	....	....	....	2	10	F	F	F	8	30
21....	27.6	F	F	F	....	....	11,079	290	60	16	50
22....	27.9	229	23	40	....	....	16,396	235	60	12	20
23....	29.5	....	....	....	....	....	....	....	....	....	....
24....	30.6	F	F	F	0	0	11,803	273	60	....	....
25....	32.0	72	5	6	....	....	2,842	98	32	17	60
26....	34.8	175	22	26	1	10	3,116	106	60	....	....
27....	39.8	116	18	20	0	0	6,985	321	60	....	....
28....	41.5	120	20	38	6	30	1,947	104	38	....	....
29....	44.8	112	15	17	1	10	8,024	412	60	....	....
30....	44.9	266	42	50	0	0	4,170	276	60	....	....
31....	53.3	....	....	....	....	....	....	....	....	....	....
32....	54.9	....	....	....	....	....	....	....	....	....	....
33....	57.6	164	18	32	5	40	F	F	F	....	....
34....	65.3	....	....	....	....	....	....	....	....	....	....
35....	66.4	285	51	50	15	60	9,072	391	60	25	70
36....	69.5	....	....	....	....	....	....	....	....	....	....
37....	81.2	....	....	....	....	....	....	....	....	....	....

* "F" indicates cases which failed through inactivity.

TABLE II

INDIVIDUAL RECORDS OF NORMAL ANIMALS EMPLOYED AS CONTROLS IN THE 10 PROBLEMS USED TO TEST EFFICIENCY IN LEARNING AND RETENTION AFTER CEREBRAL LESIONS. TOTAL TIME IN SECONDS, TOTAL ERRORS DURING TRAINING, AND TOTAL TRIALS PRECEDING THE 10 CONSECUTIVE TRIALS WITHOUT ERROR ARE GIVEN

No.	Maze III			Maze II			Maze I		
	Time	Errors	Trials	Time	Errors	Trials	Time	Errors	Trials
38	520	54	24	46	10	8	49	9	12
39	566	28	3	61	4	13	72	8	19
40	601	38	16	310	17	16	63	6	11
41	538	34	11	65	9	10	16	3	2
42	458	43	14	144	18	34	31	5	9
43	570	40	16	80	13	13	39	8	16
44	568	23	7	91	11	11	52	9	18
45	646	43	21	87	8	11	12	1	1
46	1,168	29	17	131	14	14	41	4	6
47	748	29	22	146	23	30	88	9	22
48	3,451	65	21	157	14	15	86	5	21
49	1,142	44	20	129	17	8	169	12	35
50	584	51	17	130	22	25	19	3	7
51	537	35	20	164	20	23	82	12	37
52	3,682	116	16	104	11	22	32	4	12
53	452	49	19	196	29	13	48	3	13
54	566	43	20	132	19	8	98	15	22
55	501	30	24	171	33	22	155	15	36
56	1,691	71	22	Died	......	......	......	......	......
57	1,469	31	28	Died	......	......	......	......	......
58	1,468	45	27	Died	......	......	......	......	......
59	2,007	101	36	Died	......	......	......	......	......

TABLE II—Continued

No.	Visual Discrimination		Maze III Retention			Maze I Retention			Maze I Reversal		
	Errors	Trials	Time	Errors	Trials	Time	Errors	Trials	Time	Errors	Trials
38	90	29	207	18	2	15	2	10	48	6	18
39	70	29	13	1	1	0	0	0	52	5	16
40	140	51	25	2	1	0	0	0	27	3	6
41	70	20	128	10	3	41	3	8	65	3	1
42	120	44	59	5	3	64	3	4	124	4	3
43	220	56	121	17	2	0	0	0	20	2	2
44	130	38	281	18	4	8	1	1	42	4	16
45	290	127	12	1	1	17	2	3	29	3	8
46	210	83	29	2	1	8	1	1	40	3	11
47	140	45	32	4	2	12	1	3	56	6	19
48	Died	......	......	......	......	......	......	......	......	......	......
49	120	41	0	0	0	9	2	1	48	5	16
50	Died	......	......	......	......	......	......	......	......	......	......
51	90	31	56	4	5	11	2	6	76	6	12
52	90	40	58	4	1	23	3	13	89	8	16
53	Died	......	......	......	......	......	......	......	......	......	......
54	220	64	18	1	1	23	3	12	42	5	11
55	30	16	250	16	4	41	3	8	116	8	29

TABLE II—*Continued*

No.	BRIGHTNESS-DISCRIMINATION RETENTION		MAZE IV			INCLINE BOX	
	Errors	Trials	Time	Errors	Trials	Errors	Trials
38..........	0	0	1,566	25	7	....	....
39..........	20	5	678	26	9	....	....
40..........	20	3	964	6	2	....	....
41..........	0	0	1,088	23	15	....	....
42..........	0	0	2,181	56	7	....	....
43..........	20	2	1,449	9	2	....	....
44..........	0	0	1,592	45	8	....	....
45..........	40	7	1,860	33	1	....	....
46..........	20	4	1,591	30	21	....	....
47..........	10	1	1,856	31	3	....	....
48..........	....	....	....	....	....	....	....
49..........	30	4	281	8	3	7	30
50..........	....	....	....	....	....	....	....
51..........	20	3	2,270	49	7	5	20
52..........	0	0	1,097	23	4	4	20
53..........	....	....	....	....	....	....	....
54..........	0	0	610	8	2	7	20
55..........	10	1	599	26	6	5	20

the relative influence of these variables in determining the results. The average extent of injury in the operated cases was 31.1 per cent of the total surface area of the cortex, with a range from 1.5 to 81.2 per cent and a distribution covering every part of the cortex. Figure 5 shows the combined extent of the lesions.

The average scores, total time, total errors, and total trials have been computed for each problem for all normal and for all operated animals. In computing the constants, cases which failed through inactivity (marked "F" in Table I) have been omitted. These scores with their probable errors are summarized in Table III. In this table, under the heading "Difference" the absolute difference between the groups in time, errors, and trials is included. For convenience in comparison, the average percentage of the normal score represented by the records of the operated animals has been computed for each problem. This was determined by expressing each score (time, trials, errors) of the operated group as a percentage of the corresponding score of normals, then computing the average of these percentages for each problem. These average differences are shown graphically in **Figure 6**

INCLOSED MAZES

Turning first to a comparison of the data for the three inclosed mazes, we find that, in initial learning, the operated animals are significantly inferior to the normal controls. For the most complicated maze (III) the operated animals required six and one-half times as much practice as normals, and not all upon which this average is based completed the problem. For the simple mazes the differences are less striking, but even for the simplest maze the operated required more than twice as much practice as the normals. The differences are statistically significant,

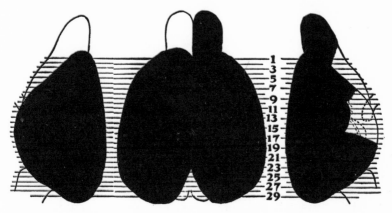

Fig. 5.—Combined extent of the lesions in animals trained after operation. In one or another, every part of the neopallium was destroyed.

being on the average eleven times their probable errors for Mazes III and II and almost five times the probable error for Maze I. From this there can be no question that the cerebral lesions were attended by an increase in the amount of practice necessary to attain the required facility in running the maze.

For the breaking-up and reversal of the original habit of Maze I the ratio of practice for operated and normal animals is about the same as that for initial learning of the same maze (2.8:1) and statistically somewhat more reliable. Inspection of the individual records for this maze shows a rather peculiar condition. Some of the animals with extensive lesions learned it without a single error, thus excelling any normal animal. Of

TABLE III

Comparison of the Average Records of Normal Animals and of Animals with Cerebral Lesions in 10 Problems. The Averages Are Based upon All Animals in Each Group Which Reached the Criterion of Learning or Completed the Arbitrary Number of Trials at Which Training Was Discontinued. Under "Difference" the Absolute Difference between the Groups Is Given, and under "Percentage" the Average of Time, Errors, and Trials of the Operated Group Is Expressed as Percentage of the Corresponding Average of Normal Animals

Problem	Normal			Operated			Difference			Average Difference as Percentage of Normal Record
	Time (in Seconds)	Errors	Trials	Time (in Seconds)	Errors	Trials	Time (in Seconds)	Errors	Trials	
Maze III	1,087±78	47±2	19±1	5,680±460	460±42	91±5	4,593±466	413±42	72±5	655
Maze II	135±10	16±1	16±1	541±29	78±4	42±4	406±30	62±4	26±4	377
Maze I	64±7	7±1	17±2	183±13	22±3	24±3	119±15	15±3	7±4	245
Visual discrimination	....	41±6	135±12	....	41±3	119±7	....	0±7	16±14	94
Maze III relearning	86±9	7±1	2±0.2	1,001±51	91±6	21±2	915±51	84±6	19±2	1,165
Maze I relearning	18±2	2±0.3	5±1	79±12	11±2	14±3	61±12	9±2	9±3	478
Maze I reversal	58±3	5±0.2	12±1	150±21	19±2	26±2	92±21	14±2	14±2	287
Visual discrimination relearning	....	2±0.5	13±2	....	3±0.5	15±2	....	1±0.7	2±3	127
Maze IV	1,365±115	26±3	7±1	5,697±610	207±25	39±4	4,332±620	181±26	32±4	599
Incline box	....	6±0.2	22±1	....	14±2	40±3	....	8±2	18±3	217

these, the ones which survived for the tests of reversal of the habit, and others also which made perfect scores in retention tests for Maze I, had unusual difficulty in breaking up the habit of turning left and acquiring that of turning to the right in this maze. Taking the group as a whole, we find a slight negative

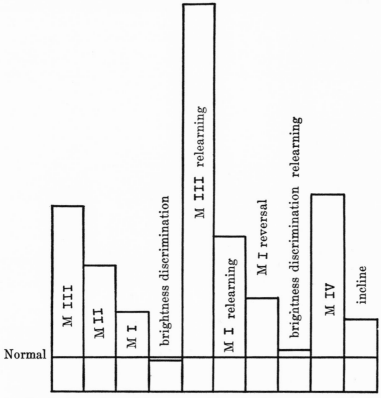

Fig. 6.—Comparisons of the averages of normal and operated animals in the 10 problems in which they were tested. The average of operated animals is shown as percentage of the normal average, indicated by the continuous line marked "normal."

correlation between the amount of practice required for learning Maze I and for reversal of the habit. This, in conjunction with observations of the behavior of the animals during training, suggests that some of them came to the problem with a definite set for turning in one or the other direction, perhaps transferred from the more complex mazes, and that this was largely influential in determining the success with Maze I. The variability of the results seems largely due to such transfer, but it is doubtful whether this has significantly altered the difference between normal and operated animals. The preferences for the right or left should have averaged out between the initial training and reversal of the habit, and we find the operated equally inferior to the normals in both.

The slight negative correlation between learning and reversal of this maze, appearing among the operated animals and not among the normal controls, suggests that the operated animals may have a somewhat greater tendency toward preservation than have the normals. The magnitude of the negative correlation and the number of cases are both too small to establish this conclusion.

The relearning tests after 40 days show even greater differences between the normal and operated cases than do the records of initial training. Relatively few of the cases with more severe lesions relearned Maze III in 35 trials, which is almost twice the average for *initial* learning of normals; and the average practice spent in retraining tests was more than eleven times the corresponding average for normals. The differences are on the average fourteen times their probable errors. For relearning of Maze I the difference is less pronounced but nearly twice as great as that which appeared in initial training.

There is clear evidence that the operated animals were inferior to the normal controls in all tests with the inclosed mazes. Since they were trained successively on the different mazes, elements of transfer and interference almost certainly entered into the results. There is at present no way of judging the relative influence of these factors on the scores of normal and of operated animals, but certainly there is no reason to believe that differences with respect to transfer between normal and operated animals are to any great extent responsible for the absolute differences in their records on any single maze.

CPEN MAZE

The open maze (IV) presents an objective complexity identical with that of Maze III. It was, however, learned by both normal and operated animals in less than half the practice required for the inclosed maze, as judged by trials or errors, although the time consumed was about the same for both mazes. This more rapid learning may have been due either to the stronger incentive provided by the narrow and somewhat unsteady support or to the addition of a visual factor which rapidly gives general orientation.

In this maze the inferiority of the operated animals is about the same as for the similar inclosed maze (5.99:1), and the differences are on the average seven times their probable errors.

DISCRIMINATION HABITS

In some ways the most surprising outcome of the experiments is the marked difference in the effects of cerebral injuries upon the learning of the mazes and of brightness discrimination. Some retardation appears in the experiments with all the mazes, yet some animals which failed to learn Maze III in eight times the practice required by normals were superior to the normals in the formation of the habit of brightness discrimination. This result is consistent with my earlier finding (1927) that complete destruction of the posterior third of the cerebrum, including the entire visual cortex, effected no retardation in the formation of the habit of brightness discrimination. As a further check upon it the following experiment was carried out.

Thirteen animals which had been used to test the influence of lesions upon the previously formed maze habit (see the experiments on localization of the maze habit reported in a later section) and which had made very poor records in relearning the maze were subsequently given initial training in the habit of brightness discrimination. Their records for maze relearning and for the visual habit are compared in Table IV. For relearning the maze they required five times as many trials as are required for initial learning by normal animals, thus giving evidence of a serious retardation. One of them failed to learn the visual habit through inactivity. The average of the others is slightly better than that of normals trained under similar conditions. The brain lesions, which are shown in Plates V–IX under numbers corresponding to the numbers of the animals in the table, produced no effect upon the ability to form the visual habit, although they had abolished the maze habit and produced a severe reduction in the capacity to relearn it.

An understanding of the difference between the results with the mazes and the visual habit will require the weighing of a number of considerations. Inequalities in incentives, in the complexity of the habits, in the sensory mechanisms involved, or in

TABLE IV

COMPARISON OF POSTOPERATIVE RETENTION TESTS FOR THE MAZE IN SOME ANIMALS SHOWING DEFINITE RETARDATION AFTER OPERATION WITH THE RECORDS OF THE SAME ANIMALS MADE SUBSEQUENTLY IN LEARNING THE HABIT OF BRIGHTNESS DISCRIMINATION

	No.	POSTOPERATIVE RETENTION TESTS (MAZE)			VISUAL DISCRIMINATION, INITIAL LEARNING	
		Time (in Seconds)	Errors	Trials	Trials	Errors
1.................	83	1,839	306	107	60	21
2.................	86	1,004	226	45	40	7
3.................	88	3,182	341	114	40	14
4.................	91	3,288	574	106	120	56
5.................	95	5,607	900	101	130	38
6.................	105	3,222	602	150	50	18
7.................	106	6,247	387	55	180	36
8.................	110	2,230	127	48	*	*
9.................	111	1,282	166	44	240	102
10.................	113	2,364	333	115	90	33
11.................	117	11,111	1,689	150	140	66
12.................	118	5,917	1,122	150	70	21
13.................	119	1,659	212	50	130	46
Average........	....	3,765.5	537.3	95.0	107.5	38.2
Average of normal animals...	....	....	....	....	135	41

* Failed through inactivity.

the character of the motor adjustments required may have been responsible for the differences. Only the first of these can be evaluated before the presentation of other evidence. In the visual habit, both hunger and punishment for errors were used to establish the habit; in the mazes, hunger alone. This suggests that the operated animals may either be lacking in appetite or be hyperalgesic. Their general behavior bears out neither supposition. They are in general more eager for food and more greedy in eating than the controls, whereas their responses to punishment are less pronounced and often suggest a considerable degree of analgesia. More convincing evidence against the importance of punishment in this connection is given by the results of earlier studies with the double-platform box. In this no punishment was used, yet the problem was learned equally readily by normal animals and by those with as much as 50 per cent of the cortex destroyed. This throws us back upon some other explanation of the difference between the results with the mazes and brightness discrimination. We must postpone further discussion of this question until data upon the relation of retardation of learning to sensory factors and to the complexity of the problem have been presented.

Not enough cases were trained on the incline to make the results of much value. The habit is formed very quickly both by normal and by operated animals, and it is doubtful whether the difference is significant. I have not used this problem long enough to acquire a dependable technique and so am not inclined to give it weight. However, there is no indication of a retardation comparable to that in Mazes III and IV; and since this habit depends upon kinaesthesis to an even greater extent than the mazes, the results may serve as contributory evidence upon the sensory factors in the maze.

CONCLUSIONS

This comparison of the massed records of normal and operated animals brings out two facts clearly. (1) The operated animals are significantly inferior to normals trained under similar conditions in the learning and retention of a variety of mazes. (2) The inferiority is not uniform but is statistically reliable for all the mazes. In contrast to this, there is no evidence of any inferiority in the formation or retention of the habit of brightness discrimination. In all cases where operated and normal animals have been compared in initial learning of this habit, the operated animals have been slightly superior to normal controls, although the differences in any one experiment have not been statistically valid. The results justify the conclusion that cerebral lesions may produce a marked reduction in the ability to learn and to remember some problems and at the same time leave the capacity with respect to other problems entirely unaffected.

The records of the first four problems show a progressive decrease in the inferiority of the operated animals until in the brightness habit they slightly excel the normals (Fig. 6). This looks like an improvement in learning ability with recovery from the effect of operation, but the fallacy of such an interpretation is shown by the records of the next problem, retention of Maze III. Here the operated animals consumed more than ten times the practice required by normals, and no animal which had failed to attain the criterion of learning in the initial training succeeded in learning in the retention tests, although these involved twice as many trials as are required for initial learning by normal animals. A similar inferiority appeared in the relearning and reversal of Maze I, although, as in initial learning of this maze, the difference was less pronounced than for Maze III. In the next problem, retention of the brightness habit, the inferiority practically disappeared. Finally, in learning Maze IV, the inferiority of the operated animals reappeared to almost as great an extent as in the first trials with Maze III immediately after operation.

The tests with Maze IV were begun at an average of 83 days after operation, with a range from 45 to 189 days. According to Donaldson's interpretation of the rate of development of the rat (Donaldson, 1924) this average corresponds to nearly 7 years and the maximum period to 15 years in the human span of life. Although we cannot use this comparison as a basis for any certain judgment of the stability of deterioration, it does give an indication of the duration of the unimproved condition in relation to the total span of life of the animal. There is no evidence for any improvement in learning ability during the time that the animals were kept under observation. On the contrary, the data show that the inferiority persisted during 3–6 months and was at all times marked for some problems and not for others. This constitutes evidence that the deterioration of the operated cases is not due to temporary shock or to any diaschisis effect but is a residual condition, ascribable by Monakow's criteria (1914) directly to the absence of the tissue destroyed.

THE INFLUENCE OF THE LOCUS OF INJURY UPON RETARDATION IN LEARNING

The series of cases includes animals with lesions in various parts of the cerebrum. In view of the emphasis which has been

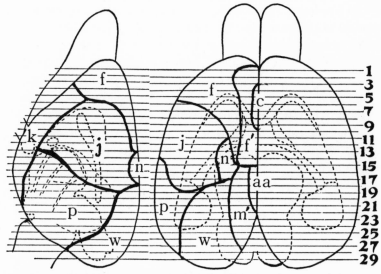

FIG. 7.—The chief cyto-architectural areas of the rat's cerebrum, modified from Fortuyn (1914) to the proportions of our diagrams. For significance of letters, see text.

placed upon association areas and upon image types in human learning, it seemed improbable that injuries in different areas should be equally effective in producing retardation of learning. We should expect either specific types of retardation associated with sensory defects or retardation following only the destruction of definite association areas. The rôle of sensory defects will be considered later. We must first consider the influence upon learning of lesions in the different cortical areas.

Figure 7 shows the chief cortical regions distinguished by

Fortuyn (1914) on the basis of cell lamination. It has been necessary to modify the proportions of his diagram to fit the one used in these studies. Since the dorsal and lateral surfaces of the cortex offer no clear landmarks and Fortuyn does not show the relation of his fields to the underlying subcortical structures, the adaptation could be made only in terms of the relative proportions of our figures. This means some uncertainty as to the boundaries of the fields, but probably no more than would exist after the accurate mapping of any single brain, since the transition from field to field is, for the most part, gradual through a broad transitional zone and, if we may argue from the condition in man, there is considerable individual variation in the limits of the different fields.

Homologies with higher forms suggest that fields f, f', and n correspond to the motor or pyramidal region, j to the somesthetic, p to the auditory, and w and m' to the visual areas of higher animals (Herrick, 1926, pp. 159–65).

The percentage of the cortex, by our method of measurement, included in each of these functional groups of fields is the following:

f, f', c, and n (motor)	17.9
j (somesthetic)	27.6
p (auditory)	28.1
w, m', aa (visual)	19.2
k (olfactory)*	7.2

* The chief olfactory cortex is the hippocampus, which was injured in a number of animals. I have not attempted to measure accurate y the extent of injury to the hippocampal structures, but rough estimates of the extent of lesion indicate that this omission has not seriously influenced results.

The cases of Table I have been divided according to the chief cyto-architectural areas involved. It is possible to distinguish, for statistical treatment, a frontal group in which the lesions extend more or less completely over areas f, f', and c and overlap j to only a very slight extent; a temporal group restricted chiefly to areas j, with some involvement of p but without overlapping f, f', or w; an occipital group covering areas w, m', and aa, invading p slightly but without involvement of j or f'; two cases with lesions restricted to p only. In addition there are cases with smaller lesions restricted to f, j, or w which can be used to test the significance of the overlapping.

DATA FOR MAZE III

The constants derived from each of the foregoing regional groups are given in Table V for Maze III. The averages for time, errors, and trials are given separately and are also combined in

TABLE V

The Influence of Regional Differences in the Position of Cerebral Lesions upon the Rate of Learning Maze III. The Cases Are Grouped According to the Principal Anatomical Areas Involved. These Are Indicated by Letters Corresponding to the Designation of the Areas in Figure 7. The Letters in Parentheses Indicate the Areas with Which There Was Some Overlapping. The Group Marked "Transitional" Includes Cases with Lesions Centering Around "n" and Invading Practically All the Fields

Area	No. of Cases	Percentage of Destruction	Time (in Seconds)	Errors	Trials	Average Percentage Normal	Correlation Trials	Correlation Errors
f, f', c (j)	5	19.3	3,049	322	83	468	0.90	0.80
j (p)	4	24.7	3,559	265	67	414	0.80	0.80
w, m', aa (p)	7	21.9	7,062	371	96	649	0.73	0.88
w, m', aa, j	10	30.1	5,893	383	81	594	0.55	0.68
p	2	6.5	2,372	47	24	148	......	......
Transitional	7	24.8	5,554	354	58.1	521	0.78	......
Normal	16	0.0	1,087	47	19	100	......	......

a single expression as the average percentage of the corresponding records for normal animals. The number of cases in each of these groups is small, so that the averages are not very reliable. They serve, however, to indicate trends; and, in fact, the differences in most cases are of such magnitude as to be of unquestionable significance.

Auditory region.—The two cases (Fig. 8) with lesions restricted to area p (auditory) had only small injuries, amounting to not more than one-fourth of the entire area, and a rate of learning not significantly higher than that of normal animals. They are not adequate for a test of the function of area p, but do serve as a control for the two groups w (p) and j (p), both of which overlap area p to an extent not greater than this. Retardation in these two groups could not have been due to the fact that both involve area p to a slight extent.

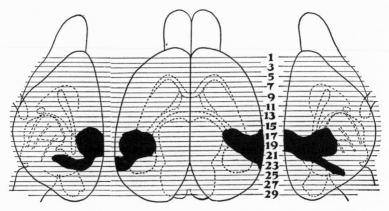

FIG. 8.—Extent of lesions restricted chiefly to the auditory area (p)

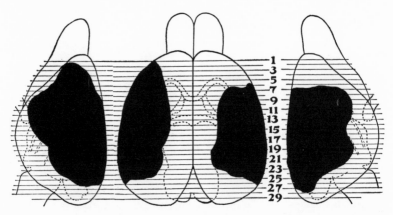

FIG. 9.—Total extent of lesions involving chiefly the somesthetic area (j), with some overlapping of the auditory and visual areas.

Somesthetic region.—Cases with lesions restricted to j (somesthetic) and p (Fig. 9) required more than four times normal practice. The slight involvement of area p in these cases is probably not significant, and the data indicate that retardation may result from injury to j.

Visual area.—Cases with lesions in area *w* (visual) overlapping *p* slightly (Fig. 10) required six and a half times normal practice. This retardation cannot be ascribed to the injury to area *p*.

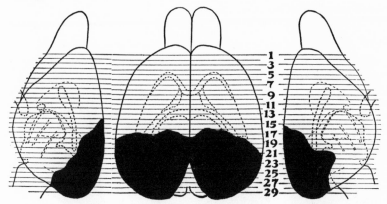

FIG. 10.—Total extent of lesions involving chiefly the visual areas (*w*, *m'*)

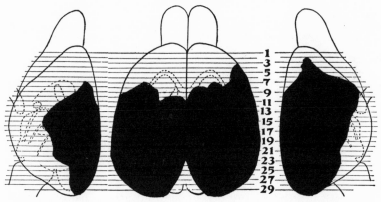

FIG. 11.—Total extent of lesions involving both visual and somesthetic areas (*w* and *j*).

Visual and somesthetic areas.—Cases with injuries involving both areas *w* and *j* (Fig. 11) required almost six times normal practice. The lesions did not greatly overlap fields *f'* or *p*.

Motor region.—Cases with lesions in the frontal area, *f* (*j*) (Fig. 12), required four and one-half times as much practice as normals. The overlapping on area *j* was slight; and one case (No. 11), with 16 per cent destruction and no involvement of area *j*, required four and one-third times normal practice. We must conclude, then, that retardation is produced by lesions in the frontal (motor) field.

Transitional region.—It will be noted on Fortuyn's diagram that most of the cyto-architectural fields approach each other very closely in the median parietal region, so that a small lesion may invade the motor, somesthetic, auditory, and visual areas

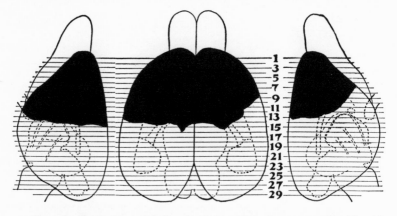

Fig. 12.—Total extent of lesions involving chiefly the motor region (*f*), with some overlapping of the somesthetic area (*j*).

A number of the cases have lesions centered in this region (Fig. 13); and since it might be interpreted as a primitive association area, these cases have been grouped separately, as "transitional." They required about five times as much practice as normals for learning.

Thus, injuries in any one of the four areas (motor, somesthetic, visual, transitional) for which adequate data are available produced a marked retardation. This ranges from 414 to 649 per cent of the amount of practice required by normal animals. These differences are great enough to be significant in spite of the small number of cases. They seem to prove that a lesion anywhere within these four areas may produce a marked retardation of learning for Maze III.

Relative effects of lesions to different areas.—The differences in effects of lesions within the three cortical areas are relatively very much smaller than their differences from the normal
condition. The groups vary in the average extent of destruction,
so that a direct comparison of the records for different areas is
misleading. From the correlations presented in a later section
we may compute the regression coefficients of time, errors, and
trials on percentage destruction. These are for time, 139 seconds; for errors, 17.7; for trials, 1.9. That is, for each increment

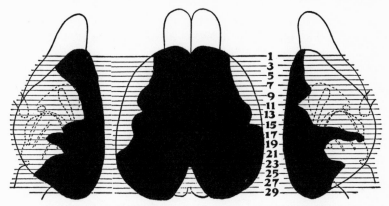

FIG. 13.—Total extent of lesions involving the transitional area.

of 1 per cent destruction we may expect an increase of 139 seconds, 17.7 errors, and 1.9 trials in the training record. Using
these coefficients, we have computed from the records of normal
animals the records to be expected from each amount of destruction. These have been expressed as average percentages of the
averages for normals, with the following result:

Group	Motor	Somes-thetic	Visual	Visuo-somes-thetic	Auditory	Transi-tional
Experimental results.........	468	414	649	594	148	521
Computed from extent of lesion	484	597	570	705	145	598
Percentage of deviation from expectation..............	−3	−31	+13	−15	+2	−14

This gives the actual deviation of the records of each group
from the records to be expected if only the extent and not the

locus of injury is responsible for the retardation. For the motor, visual, visuosomesthetic, and auditory groups the differences are slight, amounting to not more than 15 per cent of the difference between the regional group and normal animals. Lesions within the somesthetic area apparently produced less effect than lesions within other areas. This may mean that the area is less important than the others for the formation of the maze habit, but I suspect that the result is due rather to an error in measurement of the lesions. As was pointed out in discussion of the reliability of the measurements, the region where there is the greatest chance for error is the dorsolateral zone covered by the diagrams of both lateral and dorsal aspects. Measurements are subject to error of perspective and to error in estimating the overlapping of the two diagrams. Lesions in area *j* mostly fall within this zone, and a constant error of 5 per cent in the measurement of lesions (sufficient to account for the deviation of this group from expectation) might easily have been introduced. We can only conclude that animals with lesions in the somesthetic field are distinctly inferior to normals, whereas their superiority over animals with lesions in other fields is doubtful.

The data include four cases with complete destruction of one hemisphere and partial destruction of the other. In two of these cases the intact cortex included only the right motor and somesthetic areas (Fig. 14); in the other two, the right visual and auditory (Fig. 15). The average records for each of these pairs were the following:

Region Preserved	Percentage of Destruction	Time (in Seconds)	Errors	Trials	Percentage of Normal Records	Computed Percentage
Right frontal..........	67.9	10,682	1,285	150	1,500	1,135
Right occipital........	62.2	12,520	1,097	131	1,387	1,040

With very extensive but approximately equal amounts of destruction these two groups required almost exactly the same amount of practice for learning, in spite of the difference in the areas of the cortex which still remained intact.

We may approach the problem of regional differences in still another way. Only one of the 16 normal animals trained on

Maze III made more than 65 errors during training. We may therefore consider that 75 or more errors constitute some degree of retardation. There is no area common to the lesions of all

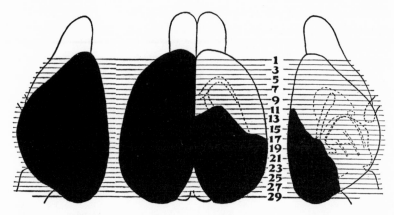

Fig. 14.—Extent of lesions in cases 34 and 35, with preservation of right motor and somesthetic areas only.

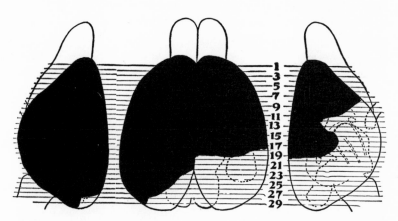

Fig. 15.—Extent of lesions in cases 32 and 36, with preservation of right visual and auditory areas only.

cases which made more than 75 errors in training (see Table I and diagrams of lesions), so that it is certain that the retardation shown by the animals of the series was not due to the destruction of any particular portion of the cerebral cortex.

The facts brought out in the foregoing analysis seem to

prove that the learning of Maze III may be retarded by injury to any of the cyto-architectural fields. The problem of the relative effects of lesions in different areas is complicated by the difference in size of the different fields and by the possible influence of the size of the lesion, irrespective of its locus. The average destruction of the cortex in the animals grouped according to locus of injury and suitable for this comparison ranges from 6.5 to 30.1 per cent of the entire neopallium. When the results are corrected for this difference in extent of lesion, there appears to be no significant difference between the effects of

TABLE VI

THE INFLUENCE OF REGIONAL DIFFERENCES IN THE POSITION
OF THE LESION UPON THE LEARNING ON MAZE IV.
ARRANGED AS IN TABLE V

Area	No. of Cases	Percentage of Destruction	Time (in Seconds)	Errors	Trials	Average Percentage Normal
$f, f', c, (j)$	4	22.2	2,287	66	22	244
$j, (p)$	2	18.2	2,300	65	14	206
$w, m, aa (p)$	5	24.1	9,079	374	60	987
w, m, aa, j	8	30.7	5,458	250	46	675
p	2	6.5	3,079	27	9	170
Transitional	6	24.7	5,029	219	42	616
Normal	15	0.0	1,365	26	7	100

lesions within different areas. We may therefore conclude that equal injuries in different cortical areas produce equal amounts of retardation. Lesions to the transitional or primitive association (?) area are no more effective than lesions in other regions.

DATA FOR MAZE IV

For Maze IV the data are less reliable, but there is indication of a distinct difference in their character (Table VI). The groups with injuries in the frontal areas require only twice as much practice as normals. Those with lesions overlapping the occipital fields, including the "transitional" group, require six or more times normal practice. The occipital groups have somewhat larger lesions than the others, but this difference is not great enough to account for the very great difference in the apparent effects of the lesions. This difference may be the result of chance, but there is some justification for considering it significant. Maze IV, as used, stood in the middle of a small room lighted from one side and with the food box near a cabinet toward which the animals frequently reached and to which some of them jumped. Repeated tests showed that when the maze was rotated to any position a trained normal animal, placed on the middle of it, would make his way by the shortest route to the original position of the food box near the cabinet. All this suggests an element of pattern vision in this habit which would involve a greater activity of the occipital regions.

If this inference is correct, we must look upon the conditions of cerebral function in the learning of the open maze as differing from those in learning the inclosed maze. A general factor of some sort is indicated from the retardation after lesions in any of the areas, but an additional factor seems to enter when the lesion involves the visual areas and the problem of pattern vision.

DATA FOR BRIGHTNESS DISCRIMINATION

The results with brightness discrimination differ from those with either maze but are consistent with earlier studies of this habit. In two previous experiments I found that the rate of formation of the brightness habit was unaltered by the destruction of the entire area whose destruction subsequent to learning completely abolished the habit. Constants for the different cortical fields have been computed for this problem as for the mazes. For all areas the results approximate very closely to the normal average. Cases with destruction in the parietal and occipital regions (visual area) learned somewhat more readily than those with frontal and temporal injuries, but these differences correspond to the relative amounts of destruction in the different areas and to the involvement of lateral ventricles and thalamus.

Results from problems involving only brightness vision are to be distinguished sharply from those in which pattern vision is concerned, for they probably deal with a much more primitive or more generalized mechanism. For pattern vision, something like a point-for-point correspondence between retina and cortex seems essential, whereas nothing of the kind is required for simple discrimination of brightness. The available evidence indicates that the rate of learning of the simple brightness habit is independent of any part of the cerebral cortex, although the habit, when formed by normal animals, shows a definite cortical localization. I should anticipate quite different results in studies of pattern vision. The slow rate at which the rat forms habits involving pattern vision has thus far prevented any adequate study of such habits.

THE DOUBLE-PLATFORM BOX

In an earlier study (Lashley, 1917) it was found that no lesion up to 50 per cent of the cerebral cortex produced any serious retardation in the rate of formation of the habit of opening the latch box shown in Figure 1. Review of these experiments reveals that the lack of effect was equally apparent for all of the areas of the cortex. When the habit is formed in normal animals, it shows definite localization in the frontal region (Hunter, 1926), yet its rate of formation is independent of any particular part of the cortex. In these respects it parallels exactly the conditions found for the habit of brightness discrimination.

CONCLUSIONS

The data on these four problems suggest three diverse types of influence upon learning, arising from brain injuries. First, for some problems, a retardation results from injury to any part of the cortex, and for equal amounts of destruction the retardation is approximately the same. The magnitude of the injury is important; the locus is not. Second, there may be a general retardation, arising from any injury, to which is added a specific retardation resulting perhaps from sensory deficiency and associated with lesion to a particular cortical field. Third, for still other habits there may be a complete absence of any effect upon learning from lesions of any extent or of any locus, within the wide limits of these experiments. The second of these types, based upon Maze IV, is no more than suggested by the results of these experiments but seems pretty well established by much clinical work with man. The first and third are clearly established in these experiments.

The results of the study of regional differences in the position of the lesions raises the question of qualitative differences in the effects. Admitted that lesions to any part of the cortex produce retardation, is the mechanism in all cases the same, or is the retardation for each locus the result of a different set of factors? The latter seems the more probable; and one naturally thinks of sensory defects or cerebral anesthesias, varying with the region injured, as the most likely cause of the retardation.

TABLE VII

CORRELATIONS (RANK ORDER) BETWEEN THE PERCENTAGE DESTRUCTION OF THE CEREBRAL CORTEX AND THE AMOUNT OF PRACTICE REQUIRED FOR LEARNING THE VARIOUS PROBLEMS, AS MEASURED BY DIFFERENT CRITERIA

	Time (in Seconds)	Errors	Trials	Average
Maze III............	0.615±0.072	0.857±0.031	0.768±0.047	0.75
Maze II.............	0.515±0.089	0.650±0.070	0.568±0.082	0.58
Maze I..............	0.191±0.167	0.299±0.159	0.164±0.169	0.20
Brightness discrimination...............	....	0.503±0.108	0.406±0.121	0.45
Retention, Maze III...	0.339±0.133	0.508±0.111	0.556±0.104	0.46
Retention, Maze I.....	.023±0.137	0.002±0.138	−0.079±0.137	−0.02
Reversal, Maze I......	0.395±0.124	0.427±0.119	0.309±0.134	0.38
Maze IV.............	0.380±0.121	0.679±0.077	0.586±0.093	0.55

The interpretation of the sensory control of the maze habit is complicated and difficult. The problem enters into all phases of our experiments, which in turn contribute to the interpretation of the sensory problem. We must therefore leave its discussion until the question can be considered in relation to the whole available evidence.

THE RELATION BETWEEN THE DEGREE OF DETERIORATION AND THE EXTENT OF INJURY

The range in extent of the lesions in the series of operated animals was from 1.5 to 81.2 per cent of the total surface area of the cerebrum, with an average of 31.1 per cent. Correlations between the magnitude of the injury and the amount of practice required for learning have been computed for the various criteria of learning for the chief problems included in this study. They are given in Table VII. With one exception, retention of Maze I, the correlations are positive and in most cases in excess of three times their probable errors. They show clearly that for most of the problems there is some relationship between the extent of injury and the amount of practice necessary for learning. Is this a true functional relationship, or is it a spurious result of some factor other than the actual elimination of tissue?

A spurious correlation might arise from any one of the following conditions:

1. The severity of operative shock might be proportional to the amount of destruction of tissue or to the amount of tissue degenerating within the cranial cavity. Thus, recovery from the operation might be delayed in cases with extensive destruction and so retard their learning. This might account for the correlations in the problem used immediately following operation, but will not account for the correlation in Maze IV, where training of the severely injured cases was begun 4 months or more after operation. It is also inconsistent with the fact that the correlation for Maze IV is as high as that for Maze II and higher than that for Maze I, although both the latter problems were used much sooner after operation.

2. If learning were conditioned by the intactness of a single insular association area, a greater percentage of large than of small lesions would invade this area by chance and retardation would occur more frequently among animals with large lesions than among those with small. In the discussion of the retardation from lesions in different areas, it has been shown that the injuries in quite different parts of the cortex are equally effective in producing retardation and that no common area is involved in all retarded cases. Moreover, inspection of Table XI and Figure 9 shows that the correlation is not due to inclusion of different proportions of retarded and unretarded cases in different parts of the range. The deviations in amount of practice form a continuous series, as does the percentage of destruction.

3. A similar argument might be advanced with respect to the invasion of subcortical nuclei. The more extensive cortical lesions are attended by injuries to the thalamus and other struc-

tures which may be the important centers for learning. I have corrected for this possibility in the case of the thalamus. Eleven of the 37 cases showed some injury to the thalamus, for the most part very slight, but in a few cases quite extensive. Correlations for Maze III were computed separately for the 26 cases without thalamic lesions and for the 11 with such injuries. They were the following:

For all cases, $p=0.86$ for errors
For cases without thalamic lesion, $p=0.83$ for errors
For cases with thalamic lesions, $p=0.86$ for errors

The omission of the thalamic cases thus reduces the correlation only from 0.86 to 0.83, and there is no reason to believe that the striatum, septum, or hippocampal structures are more intimately concerned with maze learning than is the thalamus, and so we cannot ascribe the correlation to injury to subcortical structures.[1]

It seemed, on the other hand, that failure to take the subcortical lesions into consideration might have resulted in a lesser correlation than actually exists between neural mass and rate of learning, since measurement of the surface area does not express the full extent of injury. I have attempted to correct for this in the following way:

The lesions to subcortical structures for each case are shown in Table VIII. A number was assigned to each structure, a purely arbitrary estimate of its relative importance, determined chiefly by its relation to projection tracts. These numbers were: septum, 1; striatum, 2; fornix, 1; hippocampus, 1; superior colliculus, 1; thalamus, 3. For striatum, hippocampus, and thalamus the lesions were recorded as of three grades: slight, medium, and extensive; others as of one grade only. The sum of the products of structure number by grade of injury gave an index number for each animal. Thus an animal with injury to the septum, nucleus habenula, superior colliculus, and dorsal halves of both hippocampi received the total score of 7. The animals were assigned numbers corresponding to their rank order on the basis

[1] This is not true for the habit of brightness discrimination, as will be brought out later.

of surface injury. To these numbers the indices of subcortical
injury were added, and on the basis of the sums a new rank order

TABLE VIII

RECORD OF THE SUBCORTICAL LESIONS FOR ALL CASES
INCLUDED IN TABLE I

No.	Thalamus	Striaum	Superior Colliculus	Hippocampus	Septum
1.					
2.					
3.					
4.					
5.					
6.					
7.					
8.					
9.					
10.		1(?)		1	
11.					
12.				1	
13.				2	
14.		1			
15.					
16.				2	
17.				1	
18.				1	
19.					
20.	1		3	2	
21.	1		1		
22.				1	
23.			1	2	
24.	2			2	
25.				1	
26.					1
27.	1			1	
28.		1			1
29.	1		1	2	1
30.	1			3	
31.				2	
32.	3	2	1	2	
33.		2		1	
34.	1	2		3	
35.	3	2		3	
36.	3	3	1	3	
37.	1	2		2	

was determined and correlated with the training records. This
gave for Maze III the following coefficients:

Time, $p=0.672$,
Errors, $p=0.874$,
Trials, $p=0.800$,

which represent an increase in all coefficients of about 3 per cent over those obtained by consideration of the superficial lesions only. No dependence can be placed on these as absolute values, but they serve to show that if lesions to internal structures could be accurately evaluated the method would most probably reveal a still closer correspondence between learning ability and amount of functional tissue than is shown by computing surface lesions only.

4. If retardation were due solely to the destruction of a critical amount of tissue, the inclusion of animals with injuries both above and below this quantity might result in some correlation. Table XI (page 73) shows, for the four mazes, the average amount of practice required by animals with different amounts of destruction. For Maze I there is a pronounced increase in the amount of practice required when the lesion exceeds 20 per cent; for Mazes II and III, when it exceeds 10 per cent. No such sudden increment appears with Maze IV. But above this critical point for each of the mazes the increase in practice follows the increase in extent of lesion, so that there can be no doubt that the amount of practice is a continuous function of the extent of injury.

This seems to exhaust the possible sources of spurious correlation. None of the four is adequate to account for the relationships found for the maze habits, and the conclusion seems justified that the retardation in learning is a true function of the extent of injury to the cerebrum.

ANALYSIS OF THE CORRELATIONS

Turning now to a comparison of the correlations between lesion and practice shown in the different problems (Table VII), we find a range from a high positive to a slight negative. The maximum correlation was given by Maze III. The distribution of cases for extent of lesion and errors in training is shown in Figure 16. The correlation is obviously continuous throughout the greater part of the range. The correlations for this problem are 0.61 for time, 0.86 for errors, and 0.77 for trials; are remarkably high; and are significantly greater than their probable errors.

The correlations for the other mazes are less reliable than those for Maze III, and their lesser magnitude presents some difficulty of interpretation. If brain injuries act uniformly, we should expect to find the same correlation for all the mazes, even though a relatively smaller retardation were produced by a given extent of lesion in one than in another. That is, the regression of practice on extent of destruction should be less where the absolute retardation is less, but the relative influence of different

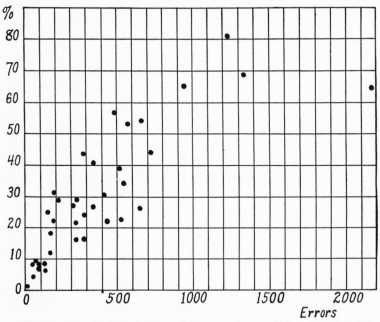

FIG. 16.—Distribution of extent of injury and errors in learning Maze III. Ordinates represent percentage of neopallium destroyed; abscissae, number of errors made during training.

amounts of injury should remain the same. It must be remembered, however, that the rate of formation of the maze habit is subject to many chance influences and that the smaller the absolute effect produced by any agent the greater is the likelihood that the effect will be concealed by chance factors, and consequently the smaller will be any correlation which depends upon the isolation of the effects of the single agent. Table IX compares the magnitude of the correlations for errors and lesions with the range of variation in errors for the different problems. The correlations follow roughly the amount of variation in the rate of learning and so bear out the conclusion that the lower correlations are due to the unreliability of the simpler mazes for the detection of slight individual differences.

From this it seems just to conclude that the correlation for Maze III represents most truly the relationship between the magnitude of lesion and the degree of retardation in learning. We have seen, from the consideration of the possible causes of

TABLE IX

COMPARISON OF THE MAGNITUDE OF THE CORRELATIONS BE-
TWEEN EXTENT OF CEREBRAL DESTRUCTION AND RETAR-
DATION IN LEARNING WITH THE RANGE OF VARIATION IN
ERRORS FOR EACH OF THE PROBLEMS STUDIED

	Average Correlation	Range of Variation in Errors
Maze III.	0.75	2,282
Maze II.	0.58	632
Maze IV	0.55	766
Retention, Maze III.	0.46	578
Brightness discrimination.	0.45	98
Reversal, Maze I.	0.38	48
Maze I, learning.	0.20	91
Retention, Maze I.	0.02	50

spurious correlation, that the constants obtained represent a real and continuous relation between the amount of destruction and the difficulty in learning. Since shock seems to be eliminated by the comparison of results with Mazes III and IV, it seems necessary to conclude that the rate of learning is dependent upon the amount of cerebral tissue which remains intact and capable of functioning. Where the range in the total amount of tissue is very great, as in these experiments, and where the learning capacity is not obscured by chance factors, as with Maze III, the correspondence is so close as to suggest that learning of this sort is a direct function of the quantity of tissue.

CORRELATIONS WITHIN SEPARATE CORTICAL FIELDS

We have next to inquire whether this quantitative relationship holds for all parts of the cortex or only within restricted areas. The correlations between extent of injury and number of errors made in training have been computed separately for Mazes III and IV for each of the principle histological areas listed in Tables V and VI. The constants obtained are shown in Table X. They range from 0.55 to 0.90, and the majority are above 0.70. The number of cases in each group is too small to give reliability to the coefficients, but all are positive and surprisingly uniform for such small samples. Considered as a whole, they give clear evidence that within each of the cyto-architectur-

TABLE X

CORRELATIONS BETWEEN EXTENT OF CEREBRAL LESION AND NUMBER OF ERRORS MADE IN TRAINING IN MAZES III AND IV, WITHIN SEPARATE GROUPS OF ANIMALS HAVING LESIONS CONFINED LARGELY TO SINGLE HISTOLOGICAL DIVISIONS OF THE CORTEX

	Motor	Somesthetic	Visual	Visuo-somesthetic	Transitional
Maze III:					
p for errors	0.90	0.80	0.73	0.68	0.78
Number of cases	5	4	7	10	7
Maze IV:					
p for errors	0.90	0.60	0.55	. . . .	. . . .
Number of cases	5	6	9	. . . .	. . . .

al fields the degree of retardation in learning produced by brain injury is proportional to the magnitude of the injury. We have seen from the data presented in the preceding section that retardation is produced by a lesion in any of the cortical fields and that diverse lesions of equal magnitude produce, on the average, equal effects. The approximately equal correlations within the single fields further show that the retardation is dependent solely upon the extent of destruction, irrespective of its locus within the cerebral hemispheres. For learning of the mazes no part of the cortex is more important than any other. This would seem to imply, as a corollary, that in maze learning the functions of the different cerebral areas are qualitatively the same. This would follow certainly if an exact quantitative equivalence of different parts were shown, but the correlations are not reliable enough to establish such an exact relationship. Further discussion of this question must be postponed until data on the sensory components of the maze habit have been presented.

CORRELATIONS FOR THE HABIT OF BRIGHTNESS DISCRIMINATION

The average correlation of $p=0.45$ for the brightness habit is puzzling. Animals with brain lesions are, on the average, slightly superior to normals in the formation of this habit, yet the greater the lesion the less readily they learn. Fortunately data are available for a check upon this result. In a previous study of the formation of this habit after occipital lesions (1927), I found a correlation of only $p=0.11\pm0.14$ between extent of injury and amount of practice for learning. In that series the maximum destruction was 43 per cent of the cortex. If we exclude all cases of the present series with more than this amount of destruction, the correlation for the remaining cases falls to $p=0.11\pm0.17$, indicating that the larger correlation is due to the inclusion of the cases with the more extensive lesions. Among these latter were several with injury to the visual nuclei of the thalamus. If we omit the cases with evident lesion to the visual thalamic nuclei, the correlation is reduced from $p=0.45$ to $p=0.22$. A similar omission in computing the correlations for Maze III results in a reduction of only 2 per cent in the coefficient for that function. Thus it appears that the greater part of the correlation for the brightness habit is the result of the inclusion of cases with thalamic injuries and that this factor does not contribute in equal degree to the correlations for the mazes.

There is evidence from other sources that injuries to the optic radiations or lateral geniculate bodies retard the formation of the visual habit, and we may safely conclude that the apparent dependence of this habit upon the extent of cortical lesion is largely the result of the inclusion of cases with thalamic injuries.

However, this does not clear up the whole problem. There remains the apparent superiority of operated over normal animals in the learning of brightness discrimination. Herrick (1926, pp. 205–9) has discussed this question in some detail. He concludes, "The presence of uninjured cerebral cortex may actually retard learning a very simple habit by reason of the complication of the processes through intercurrent cortical associations from other sensory fields." A parallel case is perhaps the readier assorting of weights in the Binet tests by children than by adults. However, the superiority of the operated animals in the visual problem is slight and may well be due to chance.

CEREBRAL FUNCTION AS CONDITIONED BY THE COMPLEXITY OF THE PROBLEM

Three of the problems used, Mazes I, II, and III, involve, in so far as one can determine, the same kind of sensory and motor processes. They differ in the length of the true path, in the number of turns to be made, and in the relative position of the turns, but present strictly comparable sensory situations. Maze IV differs from these three both in the intensity of motivation (restriction of activity to a narrow and somewhat unsteady path) and in the sensory cues which it presents. Although its objective complexity is the same as that of Maze III, normal animals required less than half as much practice to learn it as to learn the corresponding inclosed maze. Although I have included the records from it in the following tables, it must be borne in mind that it is not strictly comparable to the other three.

The three inclosed mazes present respectively one, three, and eight culs-de-sac to be avoided. This gives no measure of their actual difficulty, which can be determined only empirically. For normal animals the average numbers of errors made in learning the three mazes were the following: Maze III, 47.4; Maze II, 16.2; and Maze I, 7.3. This gives a ratio of relative difficulty for the three of 6.5:2.2:1. The mazes were used in the order, III, II, I, which means that positive transfer, due to adaptation to handling and the like, must favor the simpler mazes and tend to reduce the relative amount of practice required for learning them. In spite of this, relatively less practice is required by normal animals for the complex mazes than for the simpler.

For comparisons of the records of operated animals, a complication is introduced by the fact that not all of the animals reached the criterion of 10 successive errorless trials within the limits of the experiment, and that training was discontinued after an arbitrarily limited amount of practice. An attempt was made to set a limit for each maze proportionate to the average

trials required by normal animals, but, as it turned out, the limits
set for the simpler mazes were relatively too low. The number of
trials at which training was terminated, with its ratio to the normal average for learning, is given below:

	Maze III	Maze II	Maze I
Trials....................................	150	100	60
Ratio to normal...........................	7.5:1	6.0:1	4.0:1

Eleven animals failed Maze III; 3 failed Maze II; and 6,
Maze I. Thus, if we include all cases, we may exaggerate the
practice required for Maze III, since 150 trials on this maze represents a relatively worse record than 60 trials on Maze I. On
the other hand, if we exclude all cases which did not finish, we
throw out more of the poorer records for Maze III and so decrease its apparent difficulty in relation to the others.

However, the majority of errors are made during the early
trials, and, by basing our comparison upon errors, we avoid much
of this difficulty. The errors made by all animals in the three
mazes were the following:

	Maze III	Maze II	Maze I
Average errors, all cases....................	460.0	77.8	22.3
Ratio on Maze I...........................	20.6	3.5	1

Excluding those animals which failed to reach the criterion of
learning we find:

	Maze III	Maze II	Maze I
Average errors, all cases which learned.......	306.8	52.0	14.9
Ratio on Maze I...........................	20.6	3.5	1

The relative amounts of practice, measured in errors, required
for learning the three mazes are thus exactly the same, whether
we include or exclude the cases which failed to reach the criterion
in the allotted time. The following discussion is therefore based
upon the error records of all animals.

The relative amounts of practice required by operated and by normal animals are shown by the following figures:

	Maze III	Maze II	Maze I
Normal animals:			
Errors in learning.....................	47.4	16.2	7.3
Ratio on Maze I......................	6.5	2.2	1.0
Operated animals:			
Errors in learning.....................	460.0	77.8	22.3
Ratio on Maze I......................	20.62	3.49	1.0
Ratio of operated on normal.............	9.7:1	4.8:1	3.0:1

These figures show clearly that the relative difficulty of the complicated mazes is greater for the animals with brain lesions than for normals. Whereas the operated animals required only three times as much practice for learning Maze I as did normals, they required almost five times as much for Maze II and ten times as much for Maze III. This shows that the greater the difficulty of the maze for normal animals, the greater is the relative amount of retardation produced by brain injury.

For normal animals an increase in the number of culs-de-sac to be learned did not proportionately increase the difficulty of the problem. For the operated animals, on the contrary, increase in the number of culs-de-sac resulted in a disproportionate increase in the difficulty of the problem. This corresponds to the finding of Müller (1911) that, whereas learning by the "whole" method is advantageous for normal children, it is decidedly disadvantageous for the feeble-minded.

We must next inquire the relation of the three variables: extent of injury, complexity of the problem, and degree of retardation in learning. Is the relative increase in difficulty with complexity the same for all amounts of injury? To test this, the animals have been divided into groups by successive increments of 10 per cent destruction, and the average errors in learning the mazes computed for each group. These averages are given in Table XI. The groups are small, ranging from 4 to 11 cases, so that a good bit of chance variation is to be expected. With only two exceptions the increase in amount of practice for all mazes follows the increments in amount of destruction.

The ratios of practice required for Mazes II and III and IV

to that for Maze I are included in the table. The relative difficulty of Maze II in comparison with Maze I shows little change with increase in the extent of lesion. The records for Maze III, on the contrary, show a definite trend toward a disproportionate difficulty for the cases with greater injuries. This difference between the ratios for Mazes II and III is probably due to the fact pointed out before, that Maze II is more nearly equal in difficulty to Maze I than is indicated by the error records.

TABLE XI

COMPARISON OF THE RETARDATION IN LEARNING MAZES OF DIFFERENT
COMPLEXITY PRODUCED BY LESIONS OF
DIFFERENT MAGNITUDES

No. of Cases	Percentage of Destruction	Errors in Learning				Ratio to Maze I			
		Maze I	Maze II	Maze IV	Maze III	Maze I	Maze II	Maze IV	Maze III
8........	1–10	6.6	15.4	33.4	72.0	1	2.3	5.0	10.9
4........	11–20	7.2	40.0	33.7	266.0	1	5.5	4.7	36.9
11........	21–30	31.8	43.5	46.2	396.0	1	1.3	1.4	12.4
4........	31–40	29.3	63.2	53.0	485.0	1	2.2	1.8	16.5
4........	41–50	34.7	52.8	53.0	580.0	1	1.6	1.6	17.0
7........	50+	40.0	66.6	60.0	1,446.0	1	1.6	1.5	36.2

It may be noted in Table XI that for each of the mazes there is one short range in extent of lesion with marked increase in the amount of practice required for learning. For Maze I this increase is at 20 per cent (7.2 to 31.8 errors). For Mazes II and III it is at 10 per cent (15.4 to 40.0 and 72.0 to 266.0 errors). Whether this indicates a critical amount of destruction necessary to retard learning or is a chance variation cannot be determined from the data at hand. In the records for Maze IV there is no sharp break in continuity, so that it seems likely that it is a chance effort in the other records.

The data of Table XI with the irregularities smoothed out have been embodied in the graph of Figure 17. Amount of destruction, practice for learning, and relative difficulty of the problems for normals are illustrated as variables in the three dimensions. The absolute values are uncertain, but I believe that the figure represents a justifiable interpretation of the trend of the results.

The simpler problem offers difficulties which are not much greater for animals with brain lesions than for normal ones; and, correspondingly, the difficulty does not greatly increase with increasing magnitude of brain injury. The more complex problem,

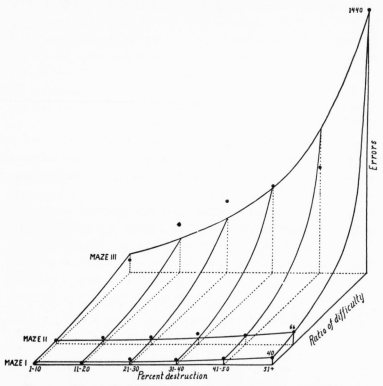

FIG. 17.—The relation between the extent of cerebral lesion, difficulty of the problem to be learned, and degree of retardation. The separation of the curves represents the relative difficulty of the problems for normal animals; the abscissae of the curves, the percentage destruction; and the ordinates, the number of errors made during training.

on the other hand, is more difficult for animals with lesions than for normals; and as the magnitude of the lesion increases, the difficulty of the problem becomes progressively greater.[2]

[2] This is borne out by the results of Cameron (1928) on maze learning after frontal lesions. He used a maze more complicated than any included in my study, and found a marked reduction of learning ability after smaller lesions than were effective in my cases.

The results with the habit of brightness discrimination do not seem to be in harmony with this conclusion, nor are those with the double-platform box reported earlier (Lashley, 1920). In the learning of both of these problems the operated animals, even with very extensive cerebral lesions, gave no indication of retardation. Yet, measured in terms of practice required for learning by normal animals, these two problems are very much more difficult than are any of the mazes. The average for normal animals on the double-platform box is 142 ± 9 trials; and for the brightness habit, 135 ± 12. The most difficult of the mazes required only 19 trials for normal animals. Thus the two problems on the learning of which cerebral injury had no effect seem to be very much more difficult than the mazes.

This apparent inconsistency in the results with the different problems may be due to any of a number of factors. We have seen that it cannot be ascribed to differences in the incentives used, but there remain possibilities of differences in the sensory or motor components involved in the habits. It may also be that the unaffected habits are psychologically more simple than the maze habits, even though the practice required by normal animals is greater. Discussion of this must be postponed until the experiments bearing upon the sensory requirements of the maze have been considered.

CHAPTER IV

THE INFLUENCE OF BRAIN INJURIES UPON RETENTIVENESS

The human clinical literature on organic amnesias deals almost exclusively with the loss of memories acquired before the cerebral insult, and we have few data upon retentiveness for material learned after recovery from the shock of the trauma. A cursory examination of cases of complete aphasia or traumatic dementia gives an impression of a reduction in retentiveness, but I know of no quantitative data on the point.

TABLE XII

COMPARISON OF RETENTION TESTS FOR NORMAL AND OPERATED ANIMALS FOR MAZES AND BRIGHTNESS DISCRIMINATION. THE DIFFERENCES ARE EXPRESSED IN ABSOLUTE TIME, ERRORS, AND TRIALS, AND ALSO AS PERCENTAGE OF THE AMOUNT OF PRACTICE REQUIRED FOR RELEARNING BY THE NORMAL ANIMALS

	MAZE III			MAZE I			BRIGHTNESS DISCRIMINATION	
	Time (in Seconds)	Errors	Trials	Time (in Seconds)	Errors	Trials	Errors	Trials
Normal animals........	86±9	7±1	2±0.3	18±2	2±0.3	5±1	2±0.5	13±2
Operated animals.......	1,001±51	91±6	21±2	79±12	11±2	14±3	3±0.5	15±2
Difference.............	915±52	84±6	19±2	61±12	9±2	9±3	1±0.7	2±3
Percentage difference on normal records.......	1,074	1,200	950	338	450	180	50	15
Average percentage.	1,014			323			33	

In our experiment on learning after cerebral injuries, tests for retention of the habits of Maze III, Maze I, and brightness discrimination were carried out at an interval of 40 days after the completion of initial training. The results of these retention tests are summarized in Table XII. The differences between operated and normals are large for the mazes and significantly greater than their probable errors. As in initial learning, the differences are greater for Maze III than for Maze I. For brightness discrimination the absolute differences are very slight and

not statistically valid. Thus in retention tests in the mazes the
operated animals are inferior to normals, whereas they are practically equal in the retention of the brightness habit. This corresponds to the finding in initial learning in which the capacity to
form the maze habits was reduced and that for the brightness
habit unaffected.

Correlations for all operated animals between scores in initial learning and in retention tests were:

$$\text{For errors, Maze III,} \quad p=0.65\pm0.08$$
$$\text{For errors, Maze I,} \quad p=0.23\pm0.13$$

Including only the cases which reached the criterion in Maze III,
the correlation for errors is $p=0.54\pm0.10$. For brightness discrimination the correlation for errors between learning and relearning is $p=0.10\pm0.15$.

For Maze III there is here a clear indication that the animals
which learn slowly tend also to make poor scores in retention
tests. This is further indicated by the correlations between the
extent of brain injury and the practice required in retention
tests. These correlations for the different criteria are $p_{time} =$
0.13, $p_{errors} =0.51\pm0.11$, $p_{trials} =0.57\pm0.10$. These show that,
within the operated group, the retention records are to some extent influenced by the extent of lesion. For Maze I the corresponding correlations are insignificant, averaging -0.01 ± 0.14
for the three criteria.

The inferiority of the operated animals in retention tests
seems to be established, but this does not necessarily mean that
their capacity to retain is affected. The relation between retention and relearning is an important problem here. The method
of studying retention used in these experiments is essentially
the savings method devised by Ebbinghaus. Where this is used,
as Ebbinghaus first used it, to test learning and retention in a
single individual under uniform conditions, it forms a justifiable
measure of retention, since we may assume that the individual's
capacity to learn in the initial training and in the retention test
is the same and that the amount of practice in the retention test
is therefore an index of the amount of loss of the habit preceding the test. For tests involving the use of two sets of subjects

differing in learning ability, the problem is more complex. If the subjects with the lower learning ability make poorer scores on retention tests, this may be a result of a greater loss of the habit, or it may indicate only an equal loss with a greater difficulty in regaining what has been lost. These alternatives may be tested either by employing some form of *Treffer* method, by which the efficiency of performance in the first trials of retention tests is measured, or by comparing the learning and retention records

TABLE XIII

COMPARISON OF THE AMOUNT OF PRACTICE REQUIRED BY NORMAL AND
OPERATED ANIMALS TO REACQUIRE THE HABIT OF MAZE III AT
AN INTERVAL OF 40 DAYS AFTER TRAINING

	NORMAL			OPERATED		
	Time (in Seconds)	Errors	Trials	Time (in Seconds)	Errors	Trials
Initial learning........	1,087	47	19	4,919	297	63
Relearning............	86	7	2	1,001	97	20
Relearning as percentage of initial learning....	7.9	14.9	10.5	20.4	32.6	31.7
Average percentage.	11.1			28.2		

of subjects with high and low learning ability for disproportionate retardation in relearning. If retention is the same in all subjects, the relative amounts of practice for relearning should correspond to those for learning.

$$\frac{\text{Initial learning, superior cases}}{\text{Relearning, superior}} = \frac{\text{Initial learning, inferior cases}}{\text{Relearning, inferior}}$$

We have attempted to apply both tests to our data in the following ways:

The average practice required for initial learning and for retention tests by normal and by those operated animals which completed learning tests, together with the percentages of initial practice required for relearning, is given in Table XIII. The initial learning of operated animals has been computed for those cases which survived long enough for retention tests; and as the greater number of deaths occurred among the cases with extensive lesions, these initial learning records are appreciably better than for the entire group given in Table II. The comparison of the normal with the operated groups shows that the animals with brain lesions not only required a great deal more practice, measured in absolute terms by all three criteria of learning for reacquiring the habit than did normal animals but also that they required relatively more practice in proportion to their initial learning records. After the interval of 40 days the normals required 11 per cent of their initial practice for relearning. Under the same conditions the operated cases required 28 per cent of initial practice for relearning.

Reference to Table I reveals the fact that 8 of the 19 animals which reached the criterion in learning and were tested for retention of Maze III failed to reach again the criterion of 10 successive errorless trials within the 35 trials allowed for retraining. This fact still further emphasizes the inferiority of the operated animals in relearning, since, if retraining had been continued until all had relearned the problem, the average amount of practice would have been still further increased and the percentage, expressed in terms of initial practice, raised above 28.

As a direct test of retention a comparison of the records for the first and second trials of retention tests of normal and operated animals is given below. For this also, only the records of animals which completed 10 successive errorless trials in learning could be used.

	Normal	Operated
Average time on first trial	68.7 sec.	233.6 sec.
Average errors on first trial	5.2	20.0
Average time on second trial	12.3 sec.	182.1 sec.
Average errors on second trial	0.9	10.6
Average time per trial in 10 errorless trials of initial learning	4.6 sec.	6.0 sec.

On the first trial of retention tests those operated animals which had reached the criterion of 10 errorless trials required almost four times as much time and made four times as many errors as normals which had reached the same grade of efficiency in initial training. The difference between the groups revealed by time required for errorless runs in initial learning is not sufficient to account for this inferiority of the operated group, so that we must ascribe it to a difference in retentiveness. The still greater inferiority of the operated animals on the second trial is probably due to the additional influence of their poorer learning capacity.

Thus it appears that the inferiority of the operated animals in retention tests with Maze III cannot be ascribed solely to the defect of the learning mechanism. In relearning, the operated cases which have learned the habit start at a lower level than do normal animals and require more than twice as much practice for relearning as would be expected from their initial retardation. There is a real reduction in their retentiveness for this habit as well as in their ability to form it.

CHAPTER V

THE COURSE OF LEARNING IN
DETERIORATED CASES

The material thus far presented has dealt with the amount of practice required to reach a certain standard of performance. Many of the animals with extensive lesions failed to reach the criterion of learning within the arbitrarily limited practice, and the comparison of their records has been based chiefly upon the number of errors made within the practice period. We must now inquire whether the failure to reach the criteria of learning indicates that the animals are incapable of improvement through practice and, if they do show improvement, whether or not this follows the laws of normal learning.

There is much individual variation in the learning curves of different animals which it would be unprofitable to report in detail. For illustration of the general characteristics of the learning curves, cases 34, 35, 36, and 37 have been selected as having the maximal lesions. The average extent of destruction in them is 70.5 per cent. For comparison with them cases 24, 25, 26, and 27 have been taken as presenting lesions of approximately half this extent (average 34.3 per cent). Individual learning curves for Maze III based on time records for the four most seriously retarded cases are represented in Figure 18, together with the average time curve of normal animals. It should be noted that the curves are constructed on semilogarithmic paper. This was necessary in order to include the great range of records upon a single graph. It results in curves with a much more gradual slope than would be produced by plotting on ordinary cross-section paper, but permits a more ready comparison of the whole length of the curves.

The individual curves are very irregular, showing far more pronounced fluctuations than are characteristic of curves for normal animals; but the general trend of all is downward throughout the course of training. This is shown more clearly

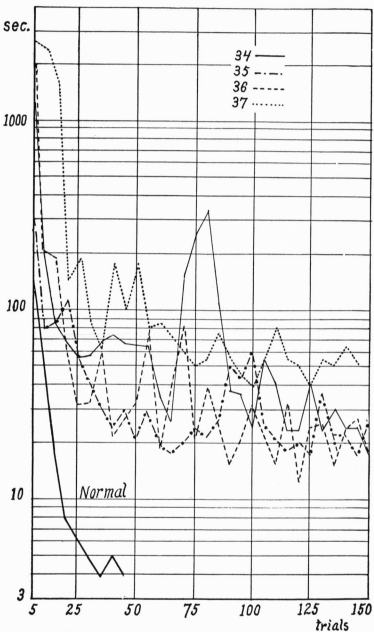

Fig. 18.—Individual learning curves for the four animals with greatest extent of destruction (Nos. 34, 35, 36, and 37). Ordinates represent average time per trial in seconds; abscissae, consecutive trials in groups of five. The average curve for normal animals is included for comparison.

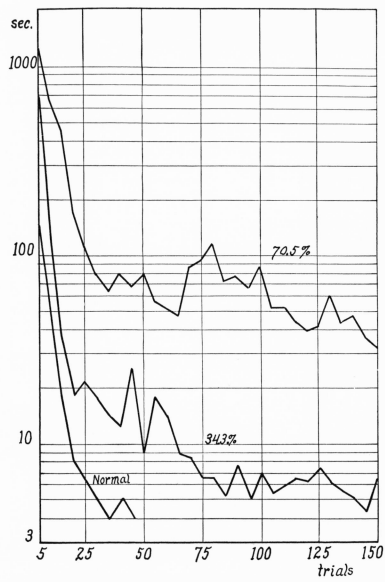

FIG. 19.—Comparison of the learning curves for time of normal animals, of 4 animals with maximal destruction, and of 4 having an intermediate extent of lesion. Ordinates represent average time per trial; abscissae, consecutive trials by groups of 5.

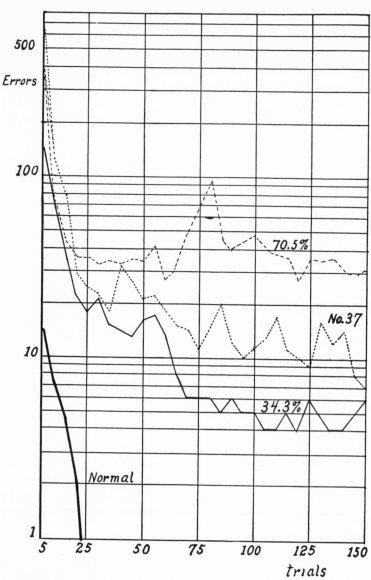

FIG. 20.—Comparison of the learning curves for errors of the same groups shown in Figure 19. The individual curve of the animal with greatest extent of lesion (No. 37) is included. Ordinates represent the average number of errors made in 5 trials; abscissae, consecutive groups of 5 trials. The average of normal animals descends to zero at the thirty-fifth trial and cannot be represented on this type of graph.

in Figure 19, based upon the average records of the four cases. There is no indication that the animals are approaching the limit of training at 150 trials.

The records for errors give a somewhat different picture. In Figure 20 the average errors for the same four animals are presented. There is little indication of improvement after the first 25 trials. However, the individual record of No. 37, the animal with the most extensive destruction, shows a continuous improvement throughout the course of training. Review of the records of the others shows that they each fell into certain stereotyped errors. Thus No. 36 in 150 trials followed a stereotyped path with 4 errors in each of 48 trials.

In Figures 19 and 20 the time-and-error scores of normals, of the four animals with maximal destruction, and of the four with half as much destruction are compared for Maze III. The curves are distinct throughout their length, which is a further argument for the reliability of the measures and the validity of the differences determined from total time and error scores.

We have little knowledge of the meaning of different forms of learning curves. The curves for these three groups do not seem significantly different in form. All show a rapid initial descent with more gradual later improvement, tending to become stationary. In so far as the curves justify any conclusions, these are that the course of learning is qualitatively the same in normal animals and in animals with all degrees of injury; that the rate of formation of the habit alone is affected, and this somewhat in proportion to the magnitude of the lesion. Animals with even the most extensive lesions are capable of continuous improvement through practice, although the tendency to stereotyped acts stops their progress at a level of efficiency less than that of normals.

CHAPTER VI

THE EFFECTS OF CEREBRAL LESIONS SUBSEQUENT TO THE FORMATION OF THE MAZE HABIT: LOCALIZATION OF THE HABIT

Previous work on the habit of brightness discrimination (Lashley, 1927), has shown a fundamental difference in the effects, depending on whether or not the cerebral injury was inflicted before or after training. If the animals are first trained and then subjected to operation, the habit is abolished by any extensive lesion within the occipital third of the cerebrum, and the amount of practice necessary for relearning is closely proportional to the extent of injury, although it does not exceed the upper range required for learning by normal animals. Destruction of any other than the occipital region does not affect the retention of the habit. If the destruction is made before training, it has no effect upon the later formation of the brightness habit, even though the entire occipital third of the cortex is extirpated. Thus the habit, once formed, is definitely localized, in the sense that it is dependent upon a definite part of the cortex for performance. Its initial formation, on the contrary, is not conditioned by the presence of any part of the cortex; the learning process is not localized, in the foregoing sense.

The present study has shown that the initial formation of the maze habit is retarded by lesion in any part of the cortex. In this respect it differs from the visual habit. Is retention of the habit dependent upon any particular part of the cortex, or is it also a function of the entire cortex?

We have data upon learning, or retention, of three other problems which seem objectively similar to the maze habits treated in the present study. These problems are the "simple maze," the inclined-plane box (Lashley and Franz, 1917), and the double-platform box (Lashley, 1920). The habit of the "simple maze" (a maze with one cul-de-sac but differing in pattern from that used in the present study) was found by Franz and the author to survive the complete destruction of the frontal third of the cortex, and I have since obtained evidence that it may survive the destruction of any other third of the cerebrum. It seems to be non-localized. The habit of the inclined-plane box showed a definite localization within the frontal third of the cortex. An unpublished study by Miss Hunter (1926) shows that the habit of the double-platform box is likewise localized in this frontal region. The rate of initial formation of the latter habit is unaffected by the total destruction of this frontal region, or by any other lesion up to 50 per cent of the cortex. This habit thus resembles that of brightness discrimination in having a definite localization of the engram and a rate of formation which is independent of any limited part of the cortex. The simple maze habit seems to be independent of the cortex for retention, yet dependent upon every part of the cortex for its formation.

These divergent results show the difficulty of making any predictions concerning cerebral function from the objective attributes of the problems. For a further understanding of cerebral functions in the more complicated mazes it was therefore necessary to carry out a study of the effects of lesions upon the retention of the habit formed before operation. An additional reason for the study—and in fact the primary one, since this experiment was concluded before that reported in the foregoing sections was begun—was to check the results of the previous experiment on brightness discrimination. In this experiment (Lashley, 1927) correlation of 0.72 ± 0.05 was found to exist between the extent of lesion and the degree of amnesia produced, as measured by the retraining or "savings" method. This relation held true irrespective of the position of the lesion within the occipital third of the cerebrum and for all ranges of magnitude. Retention was little disturbed by small lesions, no matter what their position or, presumably, what association paths were severed by them. Very extensive lesions caused loss of the habit even when they were so varied in position as to involve no significant area in common.

These facts seemed capable of either of two interpretations:

the lesions might have produced areas of scotoma proportionate to their extent, thereby reducing the chances of adequate visual stimulation in similar proportion, or the degree of retention might have been in some way dependent upon the total mass of neural tissue remaining intact although independent of the functioning of any particular areas or neurons within the general visual field. As arguments against the first alternative, the following facts were adduced. (1) Similar lesions produced no detectable effects upon the capacity to form the habit in animals subjected to operation before initial training in the problem. If scotoma had existed, it should have retarded the initial formation of visual habits as well as their re-formation in retraining tests. (2) No element in the behavior of the animals suggested the presence of blind areas within the visual field. (3) Recent observations upon brightness discrimination within scotomatous areas in man (Poppelreuter, 1925) indicate that this primitive function of brightness discrimination is not lost in cortical blindness.

Such arguments seemed fairly conclusive in favor of the second alternative and led to the tentative conclusion that, within a functional area, the efficiency of performance is conditioned by the quantity of nervous tissue available and is independent of any particular area or association tracts. This, however, introduces a conception of cerebral function so divergent from current views that we cannot accept it so long as the possibility of another and less radical interpretation of the facts remains. It did not seem possible to devise a test which would decide conclusively between the possibilities of localized sensory defect and of what I have called, for brevity, the "mass function" of the cerebrum, so long as a habit involving vision was used. But another method of settling the question, and one which should be more conclusive than a continuation of the studies of vision, is offered by a repetition of the experiment with a different type of habit. For this purpose a conditioned reaction to auditory or olfactory stimuli would be most desirable, since there is little evidence for any zonal or spacially distributed anesthesias following lesions within the cortical areas for these receptors, which could influence tests as might scotomas; but I have been unable to establish a satisfactory training technique for either of them.

A kinaesthetic-motor habit seemed next in order of suitability for the test since, even though the somesthetic system has a spacial projection on the cortex, the special arrangement is segmental and there is no probability that the production of larger or smaller areas of anesthesia will proportionately interfere with the retention of habits involving somesthesis. The maze was therefore chosen as providing a supposedly almost pure somesthetic-motor habit for which amnesia is easily detected and to some degree measurable by retraining tests.

SPECIAL METHODS

Rats were trained in Maze III, described in connection with the first experiment. After adaptation in the food compartment, they were given 1 trial on the first day of training and 5 trials per day thereafter until a record of 10 consecutive errorless trials (criterion of learning) was obtained. With the completion of these trials, training was discontinued for 10 days; then retention tests (preliminary retention tests) were given. These consisted of retraining with 5 trials per day until the criterion of learning was again attained. The animals were then immediately subjected to operation. Ten days after operation, retraining was carried out as before, training being continued until 10 consecutive errorless trials were obtained, or until 150 trials had been given, in case relearning was greatly retarded (postoperative retention tests).

Records of time per trial, total number of errors made in each trial, and total number of trials required to reach the criterion of learning were obtained for each animal for initial learning, preliminary retention tests, and postoperative retention tests. In addition, detailed notes were made on the behavior of the animals and on the character of their errors in the postoperative tests.

GENERAL PLAN OF EXPERIMENTATION

The first problem was to discover whether or not the retention of the maze habit is dependent upon special areas of the cortex; the second, to determine the relationship between the extent of injury and the degree of resulting amnesia. The report of the experiments is therefore divided into two parts—the first devoted to localization, the second to mass function—although much of the data presented is relevant to both questions. Since lesions in the visual and somesthetic area produced loss of the habit, it was further necessary to control the visual and proprioceptive factors in maze-running; and experiments to this end are reported in a later section of the paper.

The questions at issue may be summarized as follows: (1) Is the maze habit "localized" in any particular part of the cerebral cortex; i.e., is the habit abolished by the destruction of any particular area? (2) Is there any correlation between the degree of amnesia and the extent of the lesion either within a functional area or within the cortex as a whole? (3) Are qualitative differences in the character of the amnesia demonstrable, and do these correlate with variations in the position of the lesion within the general field of localization of the habit?

Approximately 75 animals were trained in the maze, subjected to operations of the cerebral cortex, and subsequently tested for retention. It was later necessary to discard the records of a number of these owing to accidental injury to the thalamus, discovered at necropsy, or to infection of the wound or the development of vestibular disease, so that only 59 relatively uncomplicated cases were obtained for statistical study. These include lesions ranging in extent from 4.5 to 50.9 per cent of the neopallium and covering all of the dorsal and lateral convexities of the hemispheres. The records of these animals are included in Table XIV and the diagram of the lesions in Plates V–X, Figures 60–118. The total area covered by all operations is shown in Figure 21. For tests of the visual factors in the maze, 12 additional animals were trained. Six of these were blinded by enucleation of the eyes after training and were tested for retention of the habit after blinding. The other six were blinded before training, which was followed by tests of the effect of destruction of the visual areas of the cortex. The records for this group are given in Table XVIII. Some of the animals which made very poor records in retention tests with the maze were subsequently trained in the habit of brightness discrimination to determine whether or not the difficulty in relearning would carry over to a different type of problem. Their records have been presented in Table IV (page 46).

RELATION OF THE LOCUS OF INJURY TO THE RETENTION OF THE MAZE HABIT

The average amount of practice required for initial learning of Maze III by this group of animals was 1,911 seconds, 54.5 errors, and 24.8 trials (Table XIV).[1] In preliminary retention

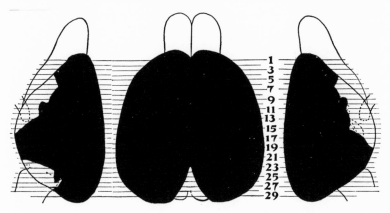

FIG. 21.—Total area explored in tests for postoperative retention of the habit of Maze III.

tests, 10 days after completion of training, their average records were 64.8 seconds, 3.8 errors, and 3.5 trials. No animal required as much practice for this preoperative relearning as the average of all for learning, and no animal required as little time or made as few errors in initial learning as the average for retention, although three learned in fewer than the average of 3.5 trials.

[1] These averages are somewhat higher than those of the control group reported in Table II (1,087 seconds, 47 errors, and 19 trials). The difference is ascribable to the facts that the mazes used were of slightly different dimensions, though of the same ground plan, and the animals of the two groups were of different hereditary strains, in one case pure albino, in the other extracted albino from hooded stock. The latter seem somewhat wilder and consequently slower in adapting to the maze.

TABLE XIV

Summary of the Records of All Cases Tested for Retention of the Maze Habit after Cerebral Injury. The Cases Are Arranged in the Order of Magnitude of the Lesions, Irrespective of Their Position. The Total Time in Seconds, Total Errors, and Total Trials in Training Are Given for Initial Training, Preliminary Retention Tests, and Postoperative Retention Tests. Subcortical Lesions Are Listed under the Following Abbreviations: N, No Injury; H, Hippocampus; C, Colliculus Superior; S, Septum; CS, Corpus Striatum; F, Fornix; r, Right, l, Left; 1, 2, 3, Estimated Grade of Injury from Slight to Severe

No.	Percentage of Destruction	Training			Preliminary Retention			Postoperative Retention			Subcortical Lesions
		Time	Errors	Trial	Time	Errors	Trial	Time	Errors	Trial	
60	4.5	1,988	39	31	315	11	18	0	0	0	N
61	4.6	2,007	50	19	0	0	0	49	3	1	N
62	4.7	958	42	17	7	1	1	0	0	0	N
63	4.8	2,515	43	12	0	0	0	0	0	0	N
64	4.9	1,221	41	13	0	0	0	25	2	1	N
65	6.1	366	38	23	60	8	12	19	3	1	N
66	7.6	1,415	43	21	70	5	3	0	0	0	N
67	7.8	837	23	13	358	17	16	17	1	1	N
68	8.3	587	39	27	247	11	14	40	2	2	N
69	8.7	2,559	90	72	124	15	12	15	2	1	N
70	9.7	1,205	40	16	174	6	9	499	31	12	rlH 1
71	10.1	1,511	93	57	0	0	0	180	8	5	N
72	10.5	1,971	39	28	31	12	1	124	23	5	N
73	10.9	853	30	23	95	5	8	4,974	700	77	rH 2
74	11.0	3,489	100	48	93	6	4	366	35	16	N
75	11.6	1,223	37	16	29	1	1	19	2	1	lCS 1
76	12.0	1,614	40	21	0	0	0	1,319	133	35	N
77	12.4	4,525	40	32	0	0	0	104	16	5	N
78	12.8	6,658	231	86	19	2	2	107	3	4	N
79	12.8	2,927	53	30	0	0	0	557	56	29	N
80	13.2	2,067	91	62	15	3	1	22	1	3	N
81	13.5	2,071	29	7	16	1	1	17	1	1	N
82	13.7	1,808	70	39	0	0	0	381	14	6	N
83	13.9	1,839	80	20	106	10	16	1,837	306	107	rlH 2
84	14.0	808	33	4	66	3	5	73	14	4	N
85	14.5	2,558	25	14	0	0	0	248	12	10	N
86	14.5	740	13	2	0	0	0	1,004	266	45	S 2
87	14.9	4,743	25	28	0	0	0	45	2	1	rlCS 1
88	15.8	345	33	20	23	1	3	3,182	341	114	N
89	16.7	973	29	13	158	4	3	79	6	3	N
90	16.7	1,303	47	25	20	1	1	710	60	28	N
91	17.1	7,273	89	30	147	3	3	3,288	574	106	rlH 1
92	18.0	2,712	58	19	11	1	1	9,695	641	150	N
93	18.1	1,507	42	24	30	3	3	11,516	689	150	F 2
94	18.3	1,957	68	49	0	0	0	313	13	3	N
95	18.8	930	44	16	0	0	0	5,607	900	101	N
96	20.6	1,013	51	28	0	0	0	63	5	1	lH 2
97	21.1	2,353	57	19	7	1	1	5,225	770	150	S 3
98	21.1	1,109	27	23	0	0	0	310	34	15	rlH 2
99	21.5	3,355	49	19	207	10	3	762	38	3	N
100	21.5	2,002	73	14	31	3	3	7,539	768	75	N
101	21.6	1,388	26	17	0	0	0	22	1	2	N
102	22.2	997	39	8	96	9	8	0	0	0	N
103	23.1	2,187	34	13	280	2	1	190	12	4	N
104	23.9	971	48	19	268	36	24	4,195	533	150	rlCS 3
105	24.2	1,020	40	23	12	2	1	3,222	502	150	N
106	24.9	1,900	13	3	67	3	4	6,247	387	55	rlH 1
107	25.4	1,642	37	21	40	1	5	11,536	1,191	118	N
108	26.2	1,700	66	17	0	0	0	5,064	742	150	rlCS 1
109	26.9	563	40	50	0	0	0	587	104	35	lH 1
110	28.3	2,088	29	12	41	2	2	1,282	166	44	N

TABLE XIV—*Continued*

No.	Percentage of Destruction	Training			Preliminary Retention			Postoperative Retention			Subcortical Lesion
		Time	Errors	Trial	Time	Errors	Trial	Time	Errors	Trial	
111.....	28.3	451	37	11	0	0	0	2,230	127	48	rlH 2; rS 1
112.....	28.6	3,136	177	49	114	5	1	2,899	304	74	N
113.....	30.2	1,638	30	41	13	1	3	2,364	333	115	rlH 1
114.....	31.1	752	23	3	300	9	5	12	1	1	rlH 1
115.....	32.1	3,804	44	32	0	0	0	11,008	464	50	F3; rlH 2
116.....	33.9	2,115	100	26	68	9	6	2,836	547	150	rlH 3
117.....	40.0	946	59	26	68	3	5	11,111	1,689	150	rlH 3
118.....	50.9	1,587	30	16	0	0	0	5,917	1,122	150	S 1; lCS 1 rlH 2; lC 1
Average..	17.7	1,911	54.5	24.8	64.8	3.8	3.5	2,221	247.4	16.0	....

These figures give a rough measure of the loss or retention of the habit for application to the postoperative tests. Their use is preferable to the comparison of each individual's preoperative and postoperative records, for the individual differences in the preoperative records are almost certainly only a matter of chance. If in the postoperative tests an animal requires as much practice as the average for initial learning, this is good evidence of a real loss of the habit resulting from the operation. If he requires no more practice than the average for preliminary retention tests, there is no evidence of any deterioration. Cases falling between these limits are of more doubtful significance. They may represent loss ascribable to the operation or only chance variations. They are omitted from consideration wherever a decision as to the loss or retention of the habit is required, and included where the relative amounts of practice required for relearning are considered.

The series of 59 cases lends itself fairly well to a study of the influence upon the habit of lesions within each of the chief cyto-architectural fields because of the great variety of lesions and the number restricted to single fields. Practically every part of the neopallium was destroyed in one or another animal of the series, as is shown in Figure 21.

Turning first to a consideration of the general distribution of lesions with reference to cyto-architectural fields, we may evaluate their effects in terms of complete loss of the habit (25 or more errors in retention tests) or of perfect retention (not more than 5 errors) as deduced from initial learning and preliminary retention tests. Selecting all cases from Table XIV (p. 92), which made not more than 5 errors in postoperative tests and combining the lesions, we obtain Figure 22. Every part of the cortex except areas *k* and *n*, the inferior margin of area *p*, and the posterior end of area *f'* was destroyed in one or another of these cases. These regions escaped destruction in many cases which

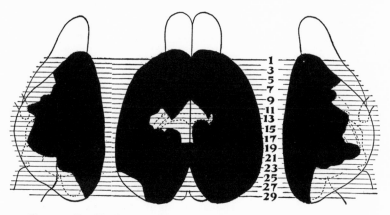

Fig. 22.—Combined extent of lesions in animals making not more than 5 errors in postoperative retention tests.

lost the habit, so that no especial significance can be ascribed to them.

If we select all cases which made more than 25 errors in retention tests, we find that there is no area of destruction common to all. For example, cases 100, 107, and 111 all show very serious loss, making from 5 to 47 times as many errors in postoperative retention tests as the normal average for learning. Their lesions are compared in Figure 23, which shows no significant overlapping between them.

It is possible, however, that non-overlapping lesions may invade the same functional field, and it is therefore desirable to analyze the data more closely with reference to the distinct histological areas.

The diagrams of Plates V–X, Figures 60–118, were classi-

fied according to the regions included in the lesions. Twenty-
three cases were found in which the lesions were restricted almost wholly to one of the anatomical areas to which diverse
functions have been ascribed because of their structure or connections. These cases are listed in Table XV, arranged in the
order of magnitude of the lesions within each anatomical field.
The combined lesions for cases in each group are shown in Figures 24, 25, 26, and 27. Many of the lesions extended into fields

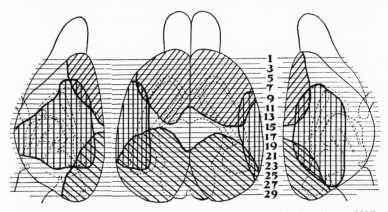

FIG. 23.—Lesions in animals Nos. 100 (////), 107 (\\\\), and 111 (||||),
which made respectively 768, 1,191, and 127 errors in postoperative retention
tests. There is no significant area common to the lesions of the three.

adjacent to the principal one involved, but in none did the overlapping include as much as 10 per cent of the adjacent fields,
which the table shows to be below the limit of effective destruction in any field. The percentage destruction, based on the total
area of the cortex, is given for each case; and the percentage of
the principal anatomical field embraced by each lesion has also
been computed from measurements of the lesions projected on
Fortuyn's diagram of the fields (Fig. 7).

In evaluating these data, it must first be noted from Table
XIV that no case with less than 10 per cent of the entire cortex
destroyed shows any significant loss of the habit, whatever the
locus of the lesion, and that serious disturbance of the habit is
rare in any case with less than 15 per cent destruction. This

makes it impossible to interpret the data on the motor (f, f', c) and auditory (p) fields, since the lesions to these were all less than 15 per cent. It may be that these fields are not at all involved in the habit function, or, if the function is dependent only

TABLE XV

Summary of Cases with Lesions Restricted Almost Entirely to Single Anatomical Fields. The Percentage Destruction of the Entire Neopallium and of the Cytoarchitectural Field Is Given. Where There Was Any Overlapping, This Is Indicated by the Letters in the Fifth Column. The Last Columns Give the Records for Postoperative Retention Tests

Fields	No.	Percentage of Cortex	Percentage of Field	Overlaps Fields	Postoperative Retention		
					Time	Errors	Trials
f, f', c	75	11.6	65	....	19	2	1
	87	14.9	83	....	45	2	1
	61	4.6	12	....	49	3	1
	66	7.6	22	f	0	0	0
	69	8.7	26	p	15	2	1
	68	8.3	30		40	2	2
j	78	12.8	32	p	107	3	4
	86	14.5	43	f	1,004	266	45
	96	20.6	49	p, w	631	5	1
	95	18.8	50	p	5,607	900	101
	111	28.3	87	p	2,230	127	48
	65	6.1	16	j	19	3	1
p	67	7.8	28	....	17	1	1
	82	13.7	43	....	381	14	6
	85	14.5	52	....	248	12	10
	64	4.9	21	f'	25	2	1
	63	4.8	25	....	0	0	0
	71	10.1	57	....	108	8	5
w, m', aa	91	17.1	68	p	3,288	574	106
	93	18.1	78	n, f'	11,516	689	150
	94	18.3	89	p	313	13	3
	107	25.4	100	j, n, p	11,536	1,191	118

quantitatively upon the cortex, that the absence of effect is merely the result of the small size of the lesions. The slight indication of an effect of the larger lesions in field p suggests that the magnitude of the lesion may be the important factor here. Additional evidence on this point will be presented later.

For the somesthetic (j) and visual (w, m', aa) fields there is clear evidence for a loss of the habit associated with the larger lesions. The effect is not invariable, but for each of the areas it occurs in 3 out of 4 cases with lesions greater than 15 per cent.

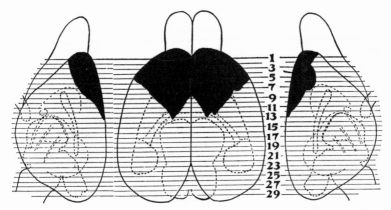

FIG. 24.—Combined extent of lesions involving chiefly the motor area, as selected for tests of localization.

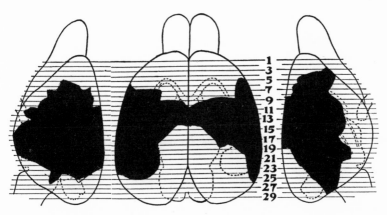

FIG. 25.—Combined extent of lesions involving chiefly the somesthetic areas, with slight involvement of motor and auditory.

There is practically no overlapping of these fields in the lesions included in the table; No. 96, which shows no loss, and 107 being the only cases which involve parts of both areas. This means, then, that loss of the maze habit may result from extensive injuries either in the visual or in the kinaesthetic field.

The obvious interpretation is that the habit is mediated by a combination of visual and kinaesthetic cues and that disturbance in either sensory area suffices to eliminate the habit. The cases

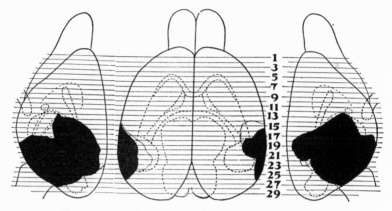

FIG. 26.—Combined extent of lesions to the auditory area

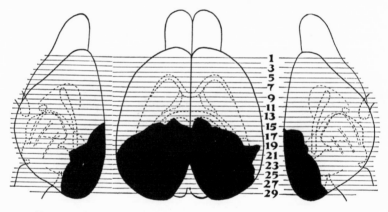

FIG. 27.—Combined extent of lesions involving chiefly the visual area

of survival of the habit after lesions restricted to one of the fields, for example Nos. 96 and 94, would then be looked upon as having learned the maze chiefly in terms of the unaffected sense.

There are, however, several facts which are opposed to any such interpretations and which point rather to an independence of any particular sensory mechanism for the execution of the habit. For an adequate interpretation of the data we must anticipate the results of some experiments which will be reported in detail later. It will be shown that retention of the maze is unaffected by enucleation of the eyes or by the section of the kinaesthetic paths of the cord, that animals blinded before training in the maze lose the habit as a result of destruction of the visual cortex without involvement of other fields, that after section of the kinaesthetic paths of the cord animals are able to run the maze in darkness without the necessity for relearning, and that there are no significant differences in the behavior of animals in the maze which correspond to the destruction of any of the anatomically specialized areas.

These facts are inconsistent with the view that loss of the maze habit is the result of a cortical anesthesia or a cortical blindness or that the function of the cyto-architectural fields in the maze habit is primarily a sensory one.

A further test of the significance of the frontal field is possible by using cases which are not wholly restricted to single fields. The data contain 8 cases which are exclusively frontal or predominantly so with some overlapping of field j. There are also 8 cases of lesions chiefly to field j with some overlapping on field f, f', n. The averages in postoperative retention tests for these two groups are the following:

	Percentage of Destruction	Time (in Seconds)	Errors	Trials
$f, f', n (j)$	16.9	1,704	202	33
$j (f, f', n)$	14.5	704	103	26

In these groups with approximately equal lesions the animals in which the motor areas were chiefly involved showed an average greater loss of the habit than those with lesions chiefly in the somesthetic areas. That the loss in the frontal cases was not due to the overlapping of field j is shown by the fact that the animals with the slightest loss of the habit showed the greatest invasion of the kinaesthetic field. This can only mean that the total destruction of the motor cortex is insufficient to produce the minimal loss which the maze technique will reveal, but that when the destruction is augmented by injury to other regions the total destruction becomes as effective in abolishing the habit as is a lesion of equal extent in other regions. There are not enough cases for a similar test with area p. This evidence, with that from the sensory control of the habit, is opposed to the localization of the maze habit in any single part or parts of the cortex. It supports, rather, the view that any lesion which exceeds 15 per cent of the total cortex, irrespective of its locus, may produce a loss of the habit. This is in accord with the findings for retardation in initial learning. In both cases the evidence was inadequate with respect to area p but seems strongly to support this interpretation of the function of the other areas.

This question of localization versus diffuse function of the cerebrum in the maze habit is a very important one for the interpretation of our data and in general for the theory of cerebral function in intelligence. We must leave its further discussion to the final summing-up of the problem when all lines of evidence have been presented.

THE INFLUENCE OF THE SIZE OF THE LESION UPON POSTOPERATIVE RETENTION

Inspection of Table XIV (p. 192) shows that loss of the habit was far more frequent in cases with extensive lesions than in those with a smaller area involved. Figure 28 shows the distribution of errors according to extent of lesion for the animals included in Table IX (p. 67) and the 5 blind cases of Table XVIII (p. 111) which completed retaining tests. Correlations based on this group between the percentage destruction of the cortex and the three criteria for relearning were the following:

$$\text{With total time,} \quad p=0.62\pm0.06$$
$$\text{With total errors,} \quad p=0.59\pm0.06$$
$$\text{With total trials,} \quad p=0.60\pm0.06$$

For the average rank of animals by all the three criteria the correlation was $p=0.69\pm0.06$.

These correlations are not as high as those found in the relearning of the habit of brightness discrimination after loss from cerebral lesions, but they are high enough to show that there is some relationship between the amount of injury and the degree of retention.

In evaluating this result, we must consider the same possible sources of spurious correlation which required control in the study of initial learning after brain injury.

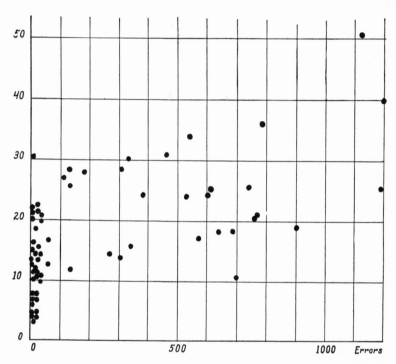

FIG. 28.—Distribution of lesions and errors in postoperative tests with Maze III. The ordinates represent percentages of the neopallium destroyed; the abscissae, the errors made in postoperative tests.

1. Operative shock and diaschisis. The possibility of effects from general surgical shock are, I believe, completely ruled out by the 10-day period allowed for recovery and by observations on the behavior of the animals after operation. In the study of retention of visual habits after occipital lesion (Lashley, 1926), increasing the period allowed for recovery from 7 to 14 days does not result in any improvement. In the retention of animals with extensive injuries, it was found that animals operated and

given initial training after an interval of 7 days all show clear evidence of relearning within the next 7 days; that is, the animals were perfectly capable of learning at a normal rate within 7 days after operation, although in others trained before operation there was no evidence of retention at this time or even 14 days after operation.

In the present experiment I have used only the 10-day interval, so that a similar comparison is not possible; but the correlations between extent of injury and amnesia are about the same for both the maze and the habit of brightness discrimination, and if shock did not enter into the latter there is little reason to suppose it more effective in the former.

Additional evidence against the importance of general shock is provided by the selective effects of extensive lesions upon learning ability for various habits. Many animals failed to relearn the maze within 150 trials (see below), making numerous errors 40 days after operation. These same animals were then trained in brightness discrimination and learned that habit in normal time, in some cases completing training within 5–7 days. We can scarcely assume that general shock was effective in retarding the relearning of the maze and immediately ineffective when the animals were trained in brightness discrimination.

Such evidence then seems to preclude the ascription of the correlations to any form of general or surgical shock. The question of a specific depression or diaschisis effect remains unsettled. As Monakow (1914) develops his conception of diaschisis, the theory is almost incapable of a crucial experimental test. He assumes that the symptoms of cerebral lesions are due to two chief causes: first, the destruction of nervous elements produces a loss of the specific functions in which those elements are concerned; second, it induces in other cells with which the destroyed elements were in functional relationship a temporary depression which interferes not only with the functions in which the destroyed elements were directly concerned but also with all others in which the depressed cells alone may have played a part. Thus he considers the immediate symptoms of injury to be a composite of the direct effects of destruction and of the indirect effects working through specific depressions or diaschisis. The depressions ultimately recover spontaneously, and only residual symptoms are admitted as evidence of the actual function of the parts destroyed.

In this form the theory of diaschisis amounts almost to an experimental indeterminism, since depression of lower vital centers which cannot be attacked by surgical methods may always be postulated in explanation of any recoverable loss. Aside from this logical objection, there are some experimentally determined facts which oppose the theory in this extreme form and seem to justify the conception of vicarious function, which Monakow is inclined to deny. In the study of vicarious function after destruction of the visual areas (Lashley, 1922), it was found that when the visual habit had been acquired after lesions within the visual areas, the destruction of no other portion of the cerebral cortex was capable of abolishing the habit. If the recoverable loss had been due to a diaschisic effect upon some other cortical center, the latter should have been destroyed in the second series of operations, with consequent loss of the habit. The experiments thus rule out the depression of one cortical center by destruction of another in situations of this type. Concerning the depression of lower centers, there is no direct evidence; but the method of recovery from amnesias following cerebral insult, as in the present experiments, is so clearly related to the learning process as to leave no doubt that it involves a reacquisition of the habits rather than a spontaneous recovery from diaschisis.

Nevertheless, the problem is complicated by some phenomena which are as yet unexplained. It is generally recognized that a slow destruction of the cerebral cortex may be accompanied by almost no symptoms, whereas sudden destruction of the same areas produces marked disturbance of behavior. It was to account for facts of this sort that the theory of diaschisis was first developed. In the present experiments two cases illustrate the slight effect of slow destructions.

Number 134 developed an infection of the cerebral tissue which continued undiscovered during retraining. His relearning was rapid, requiring 1,319 seconds and 35 trials with 133 errors.

At autopsy the entire dorsal convexities of the hemispheres were found to be replaced by a large cyst. The extent of the lesion is shown in Plate XI, Figure 134. It embraces 39.1 per cent of the entire neopallium. The habit was unquestionably lost in this an-imal, but in spite of the very extensive lesion and the active in-fective process relearning was very much more rapid than in other cases with an equal amount of operative destruction.

Number 135 was subjected to two successive operations with tests for retention after each. The first lesion was confined to the left hemisphere; the second, to the right. The extent of the two lesions is shown in Plate XI, Figure 135. A total of 54.4 per cent of the neopallium was destroyed in the two operations. The re-training records were the following:

	Time	Errors	Trials
After first operation................	567	49	9
After second operation..............	1,030	69	28

The second operation followed the first at an interval of 15 days. The total destruction was greater than that in any other animal studied with the exception of No. 59.* The retardation was, nev-ertheless, much slighter than in any case with extensive lesions produced in a single operation.

The results with these two cases cannot be strongly empha-sized, since they may represent nothing more than chance devia-tions; but they are in accord with many observations made since Goltz's studies of total decerebration, which indicate that slow progressive destruction of the cerebral cortex produces much less severe disturbances of behavior than an equivalent sudden destruction.

The meaning of such a phenomenon is by no means clear at present. To say that the loss is the result of shock and that the more rapid recovery and lesser symptoms are due to the lesser shock in the case of gradual destruction is to ignore the evident function of the learning mechanism in the process of recovery. On the other hand, the assumption that learning is alone respon-sible for the recoveries of function leaves us with the paradoxical view that learning can progress more rapidly during active destruction of tissue than after the healing.

Whatever the final solution of the problem, these phenomena are clearly not identical with those of diaschisis. All of the available evidence points to the fact that amnesias with which we are dealing here do not recover spontaneously. The lesser effects of progressive or successive slight injuries appear when the animals are subjected to training during the period of destruction; that is, when there is a counterinfluence to the disturbing effects of the lesions. The comparison of the 7- and 14-day intervals for recovery in the experiments on brightness discrimination (Lashley, 1926) shows clearly that the recovery from the amnesia occurs only through a process of relearning.

2. The possibility of a greater or lesser invasion of a single significant cortical field by lesions of different extent is ruled out by the fact that loss occurred after lesions restricted exclusively to one or another of the cyto-architectural areas. It is also excluded by the correlations between retraining records and extent of lesion given below for the single fields.

3. The character of the subcortical lesions is given for each case in Table XIV (page 92). All cases with thalamic lesions were excluded from consideration. Slight injuries to the corpora striata occurred in 5 cases, of which 2 showed little and 3 serious loss of the habit. They are too infrequent to account for the results with the group as a whole. The only internal structure injured uniformly in cases with extensive surface destruction is the hippocampus, and there are sufficient cases of loss of the habit without injury to this structure to nullify its special importance.

4. The possibility that the effects of magnitude of injury are not continuous but result only after the destruction of a critical amount of tissue is tested by the analysis of the data given in Table XVI. The cases are divided into groups by successive increments of 5 per cent destruction, and the averages for time, errors, and trials are computed for each of these groups. The number of cases in each group is small, but the cases show a definite trend toward continuous increase in practice with extent

of lesion, which is incompatible with the supposition of a critical point in the amount of destruction.

These considerations seem to rule out the factors which might give rise to a spurious correlation, and show that there is a significant relationship between the amount of destruction and the severity of the amnesia which is directly referable to the absence of the parts of the cortex destroyed and which leads to the

TABLE XVI

The Amount of Practice Required for Relearning Maze III by Animals Subjected to Brain Injuries after Initial Training. The Average Records for All Cases Falling within the Limits of Injury Shown in the First Column are Given

Percentage of Destruction	Time	Errors	Trials
1–5	14	1	0.4
5–10	98	8	2.8
10–15	669	94	20.8
15–20	3,532	329	67.1
20–25	2,776	305	61.4
25–30	3,395	355	79.1
30	5,613	769	108.5

corollary that the amount of retention is proportional to the amount of cerebral tissue remaining intact.

Is this relationship constant for all parts of the cortex or characteristic only of some parts? To test this, the cases were grouped, according to the principal involvement of cortical areas, into frontal (motor), lateral (somesthetic, overlapping the auditory area), occipital (visual), and parietal (transitional area overlapping all the chief histogocial areas) types. Correlations between the retraining records and the amount of destruction were computed for the cases within each of these groups. They are given in Table XVII. The correlations are all positive, ranging from 0.29 for trials among the occipital cases to 0.88 for trials in the parietal series. In all but the occipital group the constants are significantly greater than their probable errors. In this group there was relatively little range in the magnitude of lesions, and in general the magnitude of the correlations follows the range in extent of lesions in the various groups. There may be a closer correspondence between size of lesion and amnesia for one area than for another; the figures show only that there is a significant relationship within each of the areas; and the most probable interpretation is that this is about the same for all parts of the cortex.

Maze-learning is subject to many chance influences; the rank-difference method is not reliable for the determination of

TABLE XVII

CORRELATIONS BETWEEN PERCENTAGE OF CEREBRAL CORTEX DESTROYED AND AMOUNT OF PRACTICE REQUIRED FOR RELEARNING MAZE III BY ANIMALS WITH LESIONS PREDOMINANTLY WITHIN THE CORTICAL FIELDS LISTED

	Time	Errors	Trials	Average Rank
All cases..............	0.62±0.06	0.59±0.06	0.60±0.06	0.69±0.06
Frontal area...........	0.60±0.14	0.51±0.15	0.50±0.15	0.58±0.14
Lateral area...........	0.50±0.14	0.52±0.14	0.54±0.13	0.50±0.14
Occipital area.........	0.40±0.19	0.38±0.19	0.29±0.20	0.44±0.19
Parietal area..........	0.81±0.06	0.82±0.06	0.88±0.04	0.85±0.05

the exact degree of correspondence between two sets of variables; and the total number of cases dealt with in this study is small. To give the results a wholly reliable statistical basis would require the use of at least 500 animals. Yet even with the limited data at hand the trend seems clear enough and the results are consistent with those obtained in the experiment on maze-learning and retentiveness after cerebral injury.

It is certain that the maze habit, when formed, is not localized in any single area of the cerebrum and that its performance is somehow conditioned by the quantity of tissue which is intact. It is less certain, though probable, that all parts of the cortex participate equally in the performance of the habit and that lesions of equal size produce equal loss of the habit, irrespective of their locus.

We must now turn to the question of the qualitative effects of the lesions. Is the function of all parts of the cortex the same in kind or does each contribute special functions, such as visual or kinaesthetic memories, which are summated in the normal functioning of the habit? This question is germane to all of the work which has thus far been reported. None of the major questions raised in the course of the work can be answered finally without discussion of it, and this discussion has therefore been postponed until the questions and evidence could be considered together. This will be the task in the following section.

CHAPTER VII

THE RELATION OF REDUCED LEARNING ABILITY
TO SENSORY AND MOTOR DEFECTS

The relation of specific disabilities in learning to sensory defects was especially considered in planning the present experiments. It seemed most probable, in view of current theories of maze learning, that loss of the maze habit would follow destruction of the somesthetic area of the cortex and that, if it resulted also from lesions to other areas, the loss would correlate with defects of other sensory mechanisms involved in the maze habit. Similarly for the work on initial learning subsequent to cerebral injury, it seemed most probable that the degree of retardation would depend in large measure upon the degree to which various senses were employed in learning and the encroachment of the lesions upon the various sensory fields. Detailed notes were therefore kept on the behavior of the animals during training in the various problems, with the object of determining the degree to which the different receptors entered into the learning or re-learning of the habits; and various special tests were also carried out to control more accurately one or another sense mode. We may first consider the experimental evidence bearing upon the sensory and motor requirements of the maze and then turn to the general behavior of the operated animals for clues as to the relative importance of sensory and higher-level processes in the production of the retardation.

In his analysis of the sensory components of the maze habit, Watson (1907) showed that any of the exteroceptors might be destroyed without seriously disturbing the ability of the animals in the maze. Thus he completely eliminated smell and sight, to a large extent touch (in the vibrissae, soles of the feet, and the tip of the nose) and hearing, both singly and in combination, and was able to obtain maze learning or the performance of the previously learned habit in all cases. He did not use enough animals to establish statistically the functional equality of the normal animals and of those with sense privation, but certainly no very significant differences were apparent in his cases. The results led Watson to the belief that the maze habit consists of a chain of kinaesthetic-motor reflexes.

The analysis of the maze habit in relation to the cyto-architectural areas of the cortex failed to reveal a constant dependence of the habit upon any single field, as might be expected if the habit were dependent upon any single sensory function. These results might be accounted for in either of two ways. (1) The sensory components of the habit might have an alternative function, so that the destruction of the one sensory area would be followed by the performance of the habit through the use of other, undisturbed sensory clues. In such a case the retardation of initial learning might be due to sense privation, and the loss of the habit after lesions to the necessity of relearning the maze in terms of other senses than those primarily used in initial learning. Cases of survival of the habit after complete destruction of a sensory field would be interpreted as individual instances where that sense had played little part in learning. (2) The alternative interpretation would consider that slowing of maze learning or loss of the habit after brain injury is due primarily to defect of the associative mechanisms. The sensory interpretation of the results seems the more probable at first glance but is difficult to harmonize with Watson's findings. If, for example, learning ability for the maze is not reduced by total blindness, we should not expect it to be disturbed by injuries within the cortical visual area, unless this has some other than simple visual function. However, Watson's work was done with a maze different from that used in the present experiments; and in view of the importance of the problem in the interpretation of cerebral functions, it was necessary to obtain more direct evidence upon the relation of the cerebral fields to sensory function under the conditions of our experiments. I have therefore carried out a series of tests and observations upon sensory functions.

THE EFFECTS OF SENSE-PRIVATION UPON MAZE LEARNING

Vision.—Six animals were trained in the maze and, after preliminary retention tests, were blinded by enucleation of the eyes. Two days after this their retention of the maze habit was tested. Data on them are summarized in Table XVIII. They required an average of 33.3 trials for initial learning. The average number of trials required for learning in the preliminary retention tests was 4.6; the average for tests after blinding was

TABLE XVIII

SUMMARY OF EXPERIMENTS WITH BLIND ANIMALS. GROUP A BLINDED AFTER TRAINING WITH SUBSEQUENT RETENTION TESTS. GROUP B BLINDED BEFORE TRAINING WITH SUBSEQUENT OCCIPITAL LESIONS AND TESTS FOR RETENTION AFTER CEREBRAL OPERATION. ABBREVIATIONS: S, TOTAL TIME IN SECONDS; E, TOTAL ERRORS; T, TOTAL TRIALS REQUIRED TO REACH THE CRITERION OF LEARNING

GROUP	SERIAL No.	PER- CENT- AGE OF CERE- BRAL DE- STRUC- TION	INITIAL LEARNING			PRELIMINARY RETENTION			POSTOPERATIVE RETENTION		
			S	E	T	S	E	T	S	E	T
A.....	119	None	1,689	67	37	48	1	6	227	17	10
	120	None	800	20	23	120	7	5	140	7	3
	121	None	2,165	67	40	29	1	2	295	10	3
	122	None	2,587	35	47	12	1	1	17	1	1
	123	None	2,846	30	33	340	7	20	47	1	1
	124	None	560	12	20	156	5	4	0	0	0
B.....	125	15.2	1,542	32	14	172	4	8	559	29	3
	126	19.6	1,421	53	28	143	11	3	333	37	13
	127	24.8	8,191	56	44	32	2	1	5,544	613	102
	128	25.3	2,585	110	18	422	15	11	1,201	135	49
	129	29.2	894	22	24	140	7	3	3,371	198	13*
	130	35.4	1,324	135	43	22	1	1	2,793	792	150

* Training discontinued. Evidence of amnesia from time and error records.

3.0 The data on time and errors give equal proof that the performance of the habit was not significantly affected by loss of vision. If total loss of vision does not interfere with the habit, it can scarcely be maintained that a partial loss through scotoma can have per se any greater effect.

Six animals were blinded by enucleation of the eyes before training in the maze. They were then trained, given preliminary retention tests, and subjected to cerebral destruction of the occipital area. Their training records are given in Table XVIII. Diagrams of the lesions are shown in Plate XI, Figures 125–130, inclusive. The experiment had to be discontinued before retraining of No. 64 was completed; but from the correlations between early trials and total retraining records, given in the discussion of the reliability of the criterion, we are justified in concluding that this animal had completely lost the habit. Except for the two cases with the smallest extent of destruction, these animals lost the habit after lesion to the occipital region just as did animals with normal vision, and the degree of loss was roughly proportional to the extent of the injury. Thus it appears that lesions which in otherwise normal animals would seem to cause loss of the habit through the production of cortical blindness actually produce the same effects in animals which were totally blind during the formation of the habit. Hence it is impossible to ascribe the loss of the habit in animals with normal vision and occipital lesions to any simple disturbance of the visual function. In what way the occipital lesions interfere with the maze habit cannot now be determined, but it is certainly not through the production of a cortical blindness.[1]

Tactile sensitivity.—No direct tests were made of this since it seemed sufficiently well controlled by the form of the maze. Maze III offers tactile clues to the position of the successive doors leading from alley to alley, but as the animal passes through each of these doorways he is confronted by the alternative of a right or left turn with no tactile cues which can serve for orientation. Some other sense than touch must therefore enter in to give direction at these critical points in the maze.

Olfaction.—The wide distribution and inaccessibility of the cerebral olfactory structures prevented tests with them similar to the tests on vision. We must therefore depend upon the general behavior of animals with and without injuries to olfactory structures. In the postoperative retention tests, two animals had destruction of the connections of the olfactory bulbs (Nos. 80 and 89) without serious disturbance of the habit. Nineteen cases

[1] Munk reports that dogs, blind from occipital lesions, have difficulty in finding their way about, whereas those blinded by section of the optic nerves readily adapt to the altered conditions. The observations of Goldstein and Gelb (1918) on disturbance of spacial perception in a man with occipital lesions also suggest difficulties of orientation, although the authors applied no tests comparable to the maze.

revealed lesions to cerebral olfactory structures, chiefly the hippocampal lobes. Of these, 5 retained the habit perfectly and 14 showed greater or less loss. There were 9 cases with serious loss of the habit with no injuries to olfactory structures. Careful comparison of the cases with and without deterioration and with and without lesions to olfactory structures revealed no differences in behavior which could be related to the sensory function. The animal which follows an olfactory trail exhibits characteristic behavior (Vincent, 1915), and this was not seen in any case included in the present study. The recent study of Liggett (1928) indicates that olfaction plays less part in the behavior of the rat than we have supposed. Although not conclusive, the weight of evidence seems opposed to the view that animals with lesions to the visual or somesthetic cortex may fall back upon olfactory cues for orientation.

Proprioceptive mechanisms.—Vestibular functions in the maze are difficult to test because of the great motor disturbances which follow lesions in the inner ear, but some control is provided by the chance occurrence of three cases of vestibular infection among the animals in the experiments on postoperative retention of Maze III. (This diagnosis was not confirmed at autopsy, but the symptoms were definitely those of the common vestibular infection, of which there was an epidemic in my colony at this time.) The symptoms developed before the preliminary retention tests, and the records in these are inferior to the corresponding ones of normal animals. The cerebral lesions of these three cases are shown in Plate XI, Figures 131–33. Their training and retention records were the following:

No.	TRAINING			PRELIMINARY RETENTION			PER-CENT-AGE OF DE-STRUC-TION	POSTOPERATIVE RETENTION		
	Time (in Seconds)	Errors	Trials	Time (in Seconds)	Errors	Trials		Time (in Seconds)	Errors	Trials
131....	2,330	199	67	139	22	15	9.1	732	91	75
132....	4,115	97	43	81	12	11	9.2	1,659	212	50
133....	2,526	103	70	274	21	15	20.4	4,967	768	95

The practice required for relearning is in each case disproportionately great for the extent and locus of the lesion, and there is other evidence[2] that this type of vestibular disease produces a retardation in learning of the maze. The records on general behavior in the postoperative tests are of the same type for all three cases. The animals showed *from the first* a general orientation with respect to the direction of the food compartment; that is, they made no errors of back-tracking and pushed at the cover of the maze in the direction of the food compartment. They ran rapidly but tended to rotate and lose the right-left orientation in passing from one alley to the next. This behavior is characteristic and easily recognized. As stated above, it appeared in a few animals with cerebral lesions only, but in these no uniformity of lesion could be established. If this type of behavior is due to the destruction of a vestibular projection area, that area has no constant cerebral location.

Further evidence against the importance of vestibular function is derived from the perfect retention of the maze habit by animals with cerebellar lesions, in spite of the marked postural disturbances, rotations suggesting vertigo, and other symptoms which are sufficient to indicate that the proprioceptive mechanisms play no great part in the performance of the maze habit (Lashley and McCarthy, 1926).

The rôle of sensitivity to posture and movement in the retention of Maze III was tested by section of the afferent tracts of the cervical cord. These experiments have been reported in detail elsewhere (Lashley and Ball, 1929). It was shown that the ability to perform the maze habit was unaffected by complete transsection of the fasciculus gracilis and fasciculus cuneatus at the third cervical level, although marked disturbances of kinaesthetic sensitivity resulted. Section of all ascending tracts in the lateral columns of the cord likewise produced no disturbance in maze-running. After such lesions the animals ran the maze accurately in darkness when all other directive sensory cues seemed ruled out. These experiments show that a very severe disturbance in the kinaesthetic and organic sensitivity involves

[2] Unpub'ished studies of maze learning in animals with residual symptoms after vestibular infection.

no loss of the maze habit and that in the absence of these senses the animals, oriented from the starting-box, do not fall back upon directive cues from other sense organs.

All of this evidence opposes the view that reduced learning ability for the maze or the loss of the maze habit after operation is the result of sensory defect as such. The habits are not lost after destruction of the peripheral sensory mechanisms, and this lack of effect of sense privation is not due to shift to the use of other sensory directive cues. The habit is lost after destruction of the visual cortex in animals which were blind during learning, which indicates that the loss is due to some other than the sensory function of this area. A habit involving a specific receptor is formed at normal rate after the destruction of the cortical field for that receptor. We must conclude, then, that the probability of our findings in maze learning and retention being the product of cerebral sensory defects is very slight.

Motor defects.—Loss of the maze habit and retardation in learning might be due to some motor disturbance, of the nature either of an apraxia or of an actual paralytic disturbance of co-ordination such as to interfere with execution of the necessary movements. The latter possibilities are controlled by the following experiments.

In the experiments with spinal lesions discussed above, the descending tracts of the cord were involved as well as the ascending. In one set of animals, the pyramidal tracts were completely cut; in another, the rubrospinal; and, in the series of cases, all possible descending tracts were interrupted. All these animals ran the maze in retention tests without errors. They showed marked inco-ordinations, greater difficulty in negotiating the turns of the maze than did any of the cases with cerebral lesions, but absolutely no disturbance of orientation in the maze. This shows the ability of the rat to perform the maze habit after destruction of any of the organized descending tracts of the cord.

In the experiments of Lashley and McCarthy (1926) cerebellar lesions were attended by marked disturbances of co-ordination, but there was no disturbance of orientation in the maze attending the difficulties of locomotion.

In experiments on brightness discrimination, I have shown the survival of the habit after complete destruction of the motor cortex and serious injury to the corpora striata in the rat; and in other experiments (1914), the survival of manipulative habits in monkeys following extirpation of both precentral gyri. In several animals of the present series the motor cortex was almost completely destroyed without loss of the habit.

From these observations it seems clear that the retardation of learning and the loss of the habit from cerebral lesions cannot be ascribed to defects of the motor mechanisms as such but involve disorganization at a higher level of integration.

TYPES OF DETERIORATION IN RELATION TO CEREBRAL LESIONS

In addition to the experimental controls of sensory factors in the maze, I have kept detailed notes on the behavior of the animals in learning and in postoperative retention tests, expecting that these would reveal sensory or motor defects varying with the locus of injury. A review of these notes reveals a great deal of individual variation but no clear indication of specific sensory defects or of the loss of specific elements in the habit. An occasional animal appeared to have difficulty with the right-left alternatives in the maze, although definitely oriented with respect to the general direction of the food compartment. A few seemed less disturbed by the right-left alternatives than by the problem of general orientation, but such interpretations are uncertain, the number of cases showing the peculiarities is relatively small, and the behavior is unrelated to the locus of injury.

With respect to the more general and objective characteristics of behavior in the maze, it was possible to distinguish four types, with some overlapping. These four types were clearest in the postoperative retention tests and will be described for them.

a) The animal behaves very much as does a normal one in initial learning. He moves rather slowly, explores all parts of the maze thoroughly with few repetitions of errors, and gains a general orientation (i.e., with respect to the direction of the food compartment) quickly, so that he back-tracks only infrequently after the first two or three trials. Animals which gave evidence of some loss of the habit and which were clearly in this group are Nos. 74, 76, 83, 90, 98, 109, 111, and 115.

b) The animal seems to wander aimlessly in the maze. His movements are slow, or not faster than normal. He does not enter any cul-de-sac repeatedly but moves back and forth through rather large sections of the maze. He acquires general orientation slowly, tending to back-track after many trials. Animals in this group are Nos. 88, 106, 110, 116.

c) The animal tends to repeat the same error time and again. He usually runs more rapidly than the normal and usually dashes back and forth in one alley many times before passing through the doorway to the next. This is not due to sensory defect and failure to be stimulated by the doorway, for many of the animals pause and thrust their heads through the openings each time they pass, yet continue the perseveration in one alley; others continually retrace a complicated path through several alleys. Animals falling in this group are Nos. 73, 86, 92, 93, 95, 97, 99, 108, 112, 113, and 117.

d) The animal is disoriented and behaves much as those in group b, but runs at high speed. He does not repeat the same error as do those in group c. Outstanding cases in this group were Nos. 104, 105, and 107.

Comparison of the data on the cases enumerated above shows little if any relation between the locus of injury and the type of postoperative behavior. Marked perseveration appeared in frontal, temporal, parietal, and occipital cases, whereas animals with very similar lesions differed markedly in behavior. For example, the lesions in cases 110, 112, and 115 are almost identical, yet they come under groups b, c, and a, respectively. The behavior corresponds somewhat closely to the amount of practice necessary for relearning. The average trials in postoperative tests for the foregoing groups were: a, 41; b, 92; c, 115; and d, 134. Group a, with normal approach to relearning, showed on the average the smallest cerebral destruction.

It is clear that a tendency to perseveration or to very rapid random running is indicative of more severe deterioration, as measured in trials required for relearning, than are the types of behavior described under *a* and *b;* but this deterioration is independent of the locus of the lesion. In so far as observations on postoperative behavior could determine, there are no divergent types corresponding to different loci of injury. Practically duplicate behavior appeared in animals with frontal, temporal, parietal, and occipital lesions. In no case was the postoperative loss referable to interference with a particular receptor system. The impression given by almost all the seriously deteriorated animals was one of a more or less general disorganization involving both specific reactions to all parts of the maze and the more general orientation toward the food compartment.

The behavior of the animals given initial training after operation was in general very similar to that of the others in the postoperative retention tests. Animals with the most extensive lesions usually showed the behavior of type *c,* with rapid running and many repetitions of the same error in each trial. As in the postoperative retention tests, there were no peculiarities of behavior in any way suggestive of specific sensory defects and no special types of behavior which could be correlated with lesions in any of the cortical fields.

The results in the tests on retention of habits formed after operation are also impossible to reconcile with an assumption that the difficulties are of a sensory character. Animals which had formed the maze habit completely showed greater loss after 40 days than did normals under the same conditions. This loss cannot be ascribed to a sensory deficiency, for animals which learned the brightness habit after destruction of the visual cortex retained the habit after 40 days as well as the normals did. If a cortical sensory defect interfered with retention in the maze, it should certainly have done likewise in the brightness habit.

We thus have evidence that the maze habit is not interfered with by any purely sensory or motor defect, that the formation of a sensory habit is not retarded by absence of the corresponding cortical sensory area, and that the deterioration following lesions in different cortical sensory fields is qualitatively the same for all fields. All of this points to the conclusion that defects of the maze habit are due to some general deterioration, which affects the associative mechanism as a whole rather than distinct, qualitatively different, elements of the habit. At least it seems certain that if the deterioration is specific, it is not so for any function which can be stated in terms of simple sensorimotor adjustment.

CHAPTER VIII

DISCUSSION OF EXPERIMENTAL RESULTS

At various points in the presentation of the data it has been necessary to postpone a final discussion and interpretation until all of the lines of evidence were at hand. The report of experiments on sensory functions completes the available material and opens the way for an attempt to analyze the nature of the defects consequent on brain injuries. The data are rather intricate and are closely related to results reported in earlier papers, so that a general statement of the findings, even at the expense of some repetition, will not be out of place as an introduction to a final discussion of the problems. The results for the various separate experiments will first be summarized, then taken up in their more general relations.

SUMMARY OF DATA

Maze I (one cul-de-sac).—Data for a similar maze are available from papers by Franz and Lashley (1917) and by Lashley and Franz (1917) and from some later unpublished experiments. Results with this and Maze I are sufficiently similar to justify treating the two as a single problem. The formation of the habit is slightly retarded by extensive lesions in any part of the cortex and to some degree in proportion to the magnitude of the lesions (average correlation for time, errors, and trials is 0.20). The habit is not abolished by any cerebral injury up to one-third of the entire cortex. I suspect that there is some interference when the lesions are more extensive, but have not conclusive evidence. Retention of the habit formed after operation is somewhat reduced.

Maze II (three culs-de-sac).—The initial formation of the habit is somewhat more retarded by cerebral lesion than is that of Maze I. The degree of retardation is proportional to the magnitude of lesion (average correlation is 0.58), and retardation occurs after lesions in various loci. Data on localization and retention are not available.

Maze III (eight culs-de-sac).—After cerebral lesions the rate of formation of this habit is much retarded, is independent of the locus of injury, and is closely proportional to the magnitude (average correlation is 0.75). Retention of the habit formed under these conditions is much inferior to normal. The habit is usually abolished by any lesion involving more than 15 per cent of the neopallium irrespective of its position. The degree of loss is proportional to the magnitude of the injury (average correlation is 0.69) and probably independent of locus.

Maze IV (open maze with eight culs-de-sac).—The formation of the habit is retarded by any cerebral lesion, in proportion to its extent (average correlation is 0.55). Data on retention are not available.

Brightness discrimination.—Studies of this habit are included in several earlier papers (Lashley, 1920, 1921a, 1922, 1926). The formation of the habit is not retarded by any cortical lesion up to 60 per cent of the entire neopallium. In three separate experiments operated animals have been slightly superior to the normal controls. There is no significant relation between the extent of cortical injury and the amount of practice required for learning. The retention of the habit formed after cerebral injury is not significantly inferior to that of normal animals. When the habit has been formed by a normal animal, it is abolished by destruction of the occipital portion of the cortex (area striata), and the degree of loss is proportional to the extent of injury (average correlation is 0.72). The habit is not abolished by extensive injuries to any other part of the cortex or to the corpus striatum even when it has been formed in the absence of the visual cortex. The formation of the habit is probably retarded by lesions within the visual nuclei of the thalamus.

Double-platform box.—(Illustrated in Fig. 1.) Data on this, or on a somewhat similar problem box, have been reported by Lashley and Franz (1917), Lashley (1920), and Hunter (1926). The rate of formation of the habit is not influenced by any cortical injury up to 50 per cent and is independent of the magnitude and locus of the lesion. The habit is abolished by lesions within the frontal third of the cortex and by injuries in no other region. Not enough cases are available for a study of the influence of extent of injury upon postoperative retention.

Tests for the reversal of the habit of Maze I and learning of the incline box have not given useful data.

Sensory factors.—The tests upon the sensory and motor components of the habit of Maze III seem to establish the fact that the retardation in learning and the loss of the habit from brain lesion are not the result of any simple sensory or motor defect but can be explained only in terms of some higher-level organization. The results with the brightness habit likewise show that loss of this habit after destruction of the area striata is not accompanied by any indication of blindness to differences of luminosity, and seems referable to the associational rather than to purely sensory mechanisms.

The data raise more questions than they answer, but among their inconsistencies certain facts stand out as rather well established. In one phase or another the results with every habit indicate the importance of the total mass of tissue, and a certain lack of specificity in cerebral function.

NON-SPECIFICITY OF CEREBRAL STRUCTURES FOR LEARNING

The most surprising outcome of the work has been the number of lines of evidence pointing to the equivalence of function of all parts of the cerebral cortex for learning. When the first study of mass relations was undertaken (Lashley, 1920), I fully expected to obtain varied results from lesions in different areas, exhibited both through unlike effects upon the rate of learning and through qualitative differences in the solutions adopted by different animals. No indication of this has been obtained in any of the experiments. Selective effects upon habits already formed appear after diverse cerebral injuries, but in all tests upon learning subsequent to brain operations the effects of injuries to different areas seem to be qualitatively identical. There is no indication of a slower acquisition, which can be related to the locus of injury, of one rather than of another element of the problem.

Even where specific functions are restricted to definite areas, as in the case of the double-platform and brightness habits, the separate parts of the functional areas do not seem to have diverse subordinate functions. The reduction in efficiency pervades every part of the performance equally after lesions to any part of the functional area. It is the same, qualitatively and quantitatively, after equal lesions to diverse areas.

These facts seem to mean that the increase in efficiency of learning with increasing amounts of cortical material is not due to the aggregation of more and more diverse functions (visual, auditory, and kinaesthetic imagery or what not) contributed severally by different areas, as is implied in Munk's and Thorndike's theories of intelligence, but results from an increase in the amount or intensity of some qualitatively unitary thing which contributes to the efficiency of a variety of functions.

In a previous study I found that the function of the occipital cortex in brightness discrimination was unaffected by linear lesions which cut the transcortical fibers within the visual area, provided these lesions did not involve the destruction of a large area of the cortex. We know little of the paths of association or projection fibers in the rat's cortex. Marchi preparations after lesions to the occipital pole indicate that the majority of the occipito-thalamic fibers pass cephalad and laterad to enter the thalamus at about level 16 of our diagram. This means that many of the linear lesions described in the earlier study (Fig. 29) destroyed the majority of the occipito-thalamic fibers without disturbing the habit, although the habit is abolished by destruction of the cortical area which they supply.

The present study provides some additional evidence upon this point. In No. 1 (Plate I, Fig. 1) the lesion divided the subcortical fibers throughout the length of both hemispheres; yet this animal made a better record than any normal one which I have trained on Maze III, and was superior to the average of normals in practically all tests. In No. 2 (Plate I, Fig. 2) the lesion certainly involved a majority of the occipito-thalamic fibers without producing a significant retardation in learning.

Figure 30 shows the long axes of lesions which produced no

serious retardation in animals tested for postoperative retention of Maze III. They clearly involve the long association tracts in

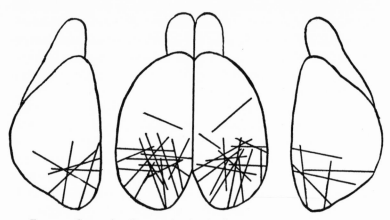

FIG. 29.—Composite diagram showing by lines the long axes of lesions which separated parts of the occipital area in animals which made not more than 5 errors in tests for retention of brightness discrimination.

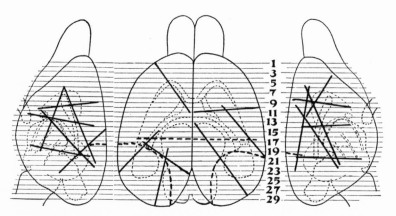

FIG. 30.—Composite diagram showing the long axes of lesions involving extensive destruction of association tracts with little disturbance of the previously formed maze habit. ———— cases making less than 5 errors; - - - cases making more errors but not seriously retarded.

every part of the cortex and indicate that, for the efficient performance of the maze habit, it is not necessary that any two cortical fields shall be in direct connection with one another.

I do not regard these observations upon the effects of linear lesions as conclusive against the specificity of function of association tracts, but certainly all of the positive evidence thus far obtained gives no indication of functionally restricted conduction within the cerebral cortex. It is perhaps what we should expect to find where the functions of different areas are not specific, and in this respect the experiments on cortex and association fibers seem in harmony.

This lack of specificity does not mean, however, that the functions of the cortex are not integrative, are not highly differentiated for each specific activity, but does imply that the functional differentiation must be largely independent of both the macroscopic and microscopic structural differentiation. How functional specificity can exist without structural is not clear from our present theories of nervous function, but in a later section I shall try to harmonize these apparently contradictory conceptions in discussing the assumptions concerning cerebral function which the facts of intelligent behavior seem to necessitate.

THE SYNAPSE IN RETENTION

We have today an almost universal acceptance of the theory that learning consists of modification of the resistance of specific synapses within definite conduction units of the nervous system. Sherrington's theory of relative synaptic resistance (1906), Kappers' theory of axone growth (1917), or Thorndike's theory of the formation of bonds (1913) may be taken as typical. In the theories nothing is implied as to the locus of these changes; for a given habit they may be restricted to a definite cerebral area or may be scattered uniformly throughout the cortex or may exist in any intermediate condition. In conformity with the doctrine of localization it is usually suggested that the region of alteration in conductivity is fairly restricted; but this is not an essential part of the theory, which, in fact, is too vaguely formulated to be capable of experimental test. Retention is thought to arise from the fact that the altered resistances, once esablished, are relatively permanent.

From such assumptions it must follow that, once a habit is

formed, its retention depends upon the stability of the individual synapses and that this stability varies either with the nature of the intercellular connections themselves, as anatomical or chemical structures, or with the action of some disruptive processes of whose nature we have still no conception.

In the experiments upon the retention of habits formed after brain injury the accuracy of performance after initial learning was for many of the operated animals as great as that of the normal controls. Their time for traversing the maze was slightly greater, but this was obviously a function of the general rate of running and not of time consumed by integration at the critical points in the maze. The peculiarities of behavior observable during learning almost entirely disappeared with the perfecting of the habit, and in final performance there were no significant differences between the operated and control animals. For the learning of the maze we have no evidence that one part of the cortex rather than another is primarily concerned, and hence cannot conclude, as we do for the habit of brightness discrimination, that after the destruction of one part another part learns vicariously. Thus there are no reasons for believing that the fundamental mechanism of the habit, once formed, differs in the normal and operated cases. The lowering of synaptic resistances to produce equal efficiencies should be equal, and equal changes should be equally stable.

But the habit of Maze III was lost more rapidly by animals with brain lesions than by normals, and to an extent somewhat proportional to the amount of cerebral destruction. This can only mean that the retention of the habit is conditioned by the total amount of functional tissue in the cortex and not, primarily, by the inherent properties of the synapses themselves. We seem confronted with the alternatives of devising some new hypothesis concerning the nature of the synaptic mechanism which will admit that its stability depends upon extrinsic factors or of facing the improbability of our whole theory of the mechanism of learning. The former can doubtless be done by making enough gratuitous assumptions concerning elementary neurophysiology. We might cite the facts of retroactive inhibition as evidence for extrinsic disruptive forces acting on the synapse, and posit inhibit-ors and inhibitors of inhibitors, as Pavlov (1927) has done; but the truth is that our hypotheses have so far exceeded our facts as to be beyond any experimental test, and the piling on of a few more speculations is likely to make the whole structure collapse of its own weight.

The synapse is, physiologically, a convention to describe the polarity of conduction in the nervous system of higher animals, together with some similarities of function in the central nervous system and in the neuromuscular junction. That these functions are due to the action of the intercellular membranes has not been directly demonstrated. Learning or processes so closely allied to learning that we cannot characterize their differences (adaptation, change in the sense of reaction, modifiability of behavior), have been found in organisms with a syncytial type of nervous system, so that it is not clear that the synapse is either essential or important for learning. The convention has been useful for dealing with some of the simpler physiological reactions but is not on that account the *sine qua non* of neurological theory.

THE MASS FACTOR IN CEREBRAL FUNCTION

Three types of experiments have now given significant cor-relations between the extent of cerebral lesion and the efficiency of performance of a habit mechanism. The types seem sufficient-ly diverse to avoid common sources of error. The rate of learn-ing of the four mazes reported in this study is clearly a function of the total mass of tissue, and the evidence presented indicates that retentiveness *as such* for these habits is conditioned in the same way. Postoperative tests with Maze III show a similar re-lationship to the mass of the cortex as a whole. The correspond-ence is less close than for initial learning but is nevertheless significant. In the habit of brightness discrimination the mass effect is restricted to the performance of the habit after it has been acquired and to the occipital third of the cortex instead of to the entire cerebrum, as in the maze habits. Figure 31 shows the distribution of errors on percentage destruction for retention of the brightness habit. It is exhibited within a quantitative

range of destruction which produces less definite effects in the
maze habit, and this may be taken as an indication that with
the restriction of the mass function to the occipital pole there is
established a more delicate equilibrium than among the parts of
the cortex as a whole.

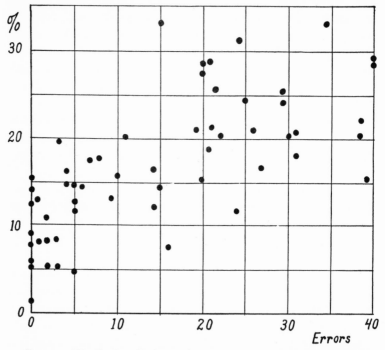

FIG. 31.—Distribution of lesions and errors in postoperative retention tests for
the habit of brightness discrimination. The ordinates represent the percentage of
cortex destroyed; abscissae, total number of errors preceding 30 consecutive errorless trials.

The only possible source of spurious correlation for the
brightness habit seemed to be the production of scotoma. The
controls of sensory function in the maze seem to rule out any similar possibility and leave the correlation as representative of some
actual interference with the associative mechanisms of the cortex.
The relationship is not an artifact arising from some peculiarity
of the methods of training, from the shock of operation, from
sense privation, or from the production of different amounts of
paralysis. It can be interpreted only as a real relationship be-

tween the amount of cerebral tissue and the efficiency of its action.

In previous discussions of this factor of mass (1926) I pointed out that it might be either a result of the participation of a large number of equivalent conditioned reflex arcs passing through different parts of the cortex or an indication of some less specific dynamic function. If we assume that with improvement in a habit more and more similar bonds are formed among its elements, which in turn are responsible for increased efficiency in its performance, then partial destruction of these bonds might produce a loss proportional to the number rendered nonfunctional.

Evidence was adduced from the lack of effects of linear lesions that the reduplicated bonds could not be transcortical, and arguments against the existence of equivalent conduction systems in different parts of the cortex were suggested from the complexity of the habit and the failure of lesions ever to separate it into component parts; but the problem could not then be conclusively settled on the existing evidence.

The present experiments contribute three sets of data which further oppose the reduplication hypothesis:

1. They make it possible to extend the test of section of association fibers to those connecting the cortex with lower centers and give additional data on the effects of the interruption of large numbers of transcortical fibers. The thalamico-occipital fibers probably pass cephalad from the thalamus in the posterior part of the internal capsule, turn upward and outward at about level 15 of our diagrams, and, after passing around the anterior margin of the hoppocampal lobes, turn caudad, in the thin sheet of white matter underlying the cortex, to reach the area striata. Thus any lesion which penetrates the fiber layer (as do all in the present studies) at level 17 or farther back, must interrupt the projection tracts of the areas directly behind the lesion.

In the postoperative retention tests were 8 cases with rather narrow transverse lesions within this general area. These were Nos. 65, 67, 69, 70, 73, 74, 78, and 82. The average extent of lesions in these cases was 10.1 per cent. Their average errors in retraining were 14.0. The caudal margins of the lesions in these cases are shown in Figure 32. The majority of them must have severed at least half of the projection fibers of the occipital cortex, yet the average loss of the habit which they produced is not greater than expected from the actual magnitude of the lesion to the cortex alone. Numbers 101, 105, 107, 110, 113, and 116 had destruction of the areas caudad to the regions involved in the foregoing cases. Their average destruction was 27.3 per cent, and the average of their errors in postoperative retention tests

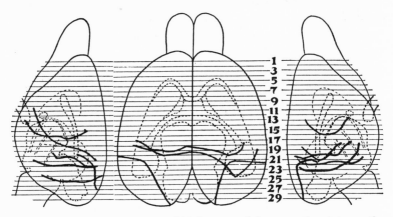

Fig. 32.—Diagram of lesions which interrupted the connections between the thalamus and the occipital cortex without serious disturbance of behavior.

was 456. Thus the destruction of the areas supplied by the projection fibers produces much more serious disturbance than an extensive injury to the fibers.

In training after operation there were 3 cases with linear injuries interrupting thalamico-occipital bundles. These were Nos. 2, 7, and 9. Their average destruction was 8.1 per cent; and average errors in learning, 87.3. This is considerably under the expectation from the regression coefficient for the whole group and indicates that the partial interruption of the projection tracts to the occipital areas did not produce a retardation.

The evidence upon this point is not yet complete, for every cortical lesion interrupts some association tracts as well as destroys a definite amount of cortex, so that our standard of comparison for lesions of any size may be partly determined by the interruption of fibers; but if this is accepted as a rejoinder to the preceding argument, it leads to the further conclusion that for learning or retention of the maze habit all projection and association paths are equipotential.

2. Contribution to the efficiency of performance of a habit by the summated action of equivalent bonds is understandable for habits which have already been formed. It is less obvious how their formation could be retarded by a reduction in the number of possible bonds before the bonds have been formed. For this to occur would require that only a limited number of bonds for any given performance can be formed readily in any part of the cortex—an assumption which is contradicted by the results with the visual discrimination habit which normally involves only the occipital cortex, yet is formed with equal facility in the absence of this area.

3. Even granting that such a limitation exists, it is still more difficult to understand, in terms of reduplication of bonds, how a habit which has been learned to equal efficiency of performance (i.e., to the establishment of equal numbers of bonds) by two animals with unequal amounts of cortex should be more effectively retained by one than by the other, in accord with the amount of functional tissue.

The evidence thus seems opposed to the hypothesis that the correlations found are due to the reduplication of equivalent arcs, and we are forced to postulate some mechanism distributed throughout the cerebral cortex and capable of facilitating a variety of activities by its total mass rather than by specific integrations.

The results are in accord with a view which Bianchi (1922) has formulated clearly for the purpose of refutation:

Suppose for a moment that intelligence emanates from the cortical fields (arcs) [sic] like electricity from electric batteries; it becomes more intense and reaches a higher potential as the number of areas increases, just as the intensity of the electric current, ceteris paribus, increases with an increased number of batteries.

Far from accepting Bianchi's criticisms of such a theory, I find it the only expression which will adequately cover the facts reported.

CHAPTER IX

THE NATURE OF THE DETERIORATION
FOLLOWING CEREBRAL LESIONS

The experimental data upon learning after brain injuries seem conflicting. On the one hand, there is more or less retardation in maze learning for every type of maze studied, and a significant reduction of retentiveness for at least the most complicated of the mazes. On the other hand, neither learning nor retentiveness for the brightness habit is affected by any previous amount or locus of cerebral injury. With the visual habit that of the double-platform box must be classed, for its rate of formation is likewise unaffected by extensive cerebral lesions. Some fundamental difference between the two groups of habits is shown not only by the diverse records in initial learning after cortical destruction but also by studies of postoperative retention. The maze habits show no definite localization when formed; the brightness habit is clearly associated with the area striata (Lashley, 1927) and the problem box with the frontal region (Lashley and Franz, 1917; Hunter, 1926).

SIGNIFICANCE OF DIFFERENT RESULTS IN THE FORMATION OF
MAZE AND DISCRIMINATION HABITS

Is the retardation in the mazes due to the loss of some function which is specific for maze learning, or is it indicative of some more general deficiency comparable to dementia? If the former, what, specifically, is the nature of the defect; if the latter, how can we account for the normal rate of formation of the other habits? The two habits differed in the sensory factors involved and in the incentives used for learning. We must first consider whether these are sufficient to account for the unlike influences of cerebral injury.

Sensory factors.—From the data on the brightness habit it is clear that a retardation of learning is not produced by a destruction of the chief cortical area normally involved in the sensory processes underlying the habit. The various lines of evidence on the sensory components of the maze habit seem also to rule out any important influence of purely sensory defects in the retardation of maze learning. Peripheral sense privation does not produce the types of behavior characteristic of lesions in the cortical sensory fields. Moreover, the double-platform box, which seems to involve the same sensorimotor adjustments as the mazes, behaves like the brightness habit in relation to cortical injury. There is thus no justification for ascribing the difference between these two types of habits to the destruction or survival of different cerebral sensory mechanisms. The explanation of the differences must be sought at a higher level of integration.

The relation of incentives to retardation.—In the mazes hunger was used as an incentive to learning; in the brightness box, a combination of hunger and punishment for errors. But the difference cannot be ascribed to the punishment, for hunger was the sole incentive for learning with the double-platform box, and with it animals having brain lesions showed no retardation. Furthermore, if we can judge at all by the general behavior of the animals, the hunger incentive is stronger in the severely deteriorated cases than in normal animals. They are more voracious, more constantly active in the maze before they reach the food, and some of them will eat far larger quantities of food than normal animals, stuffing themselves until it seems that they must burst. On the other hand, they seem as a rule less sensitive to punishment (faradization) than are normal animals.

These facts seem to rule out differences in incentives as an important factor in differentiating the two types of habit.

The probable simplicity of the latch-box and discrimination habits.—The double-platform box requires 142 ± 9 trials for learning by normal animals; the brightness habit, about 135 ± 12 trials. The most difficult of the mazes studied required an average of only 19 trials for learing. Thus the two problems on the learning of which cerebral injury had no effect seem to be enormously more difficult than the mazes, in which the effects of cerebral lesion were most pronounced. But there are other relevant facts. The typical learning curve for both the inclined-plane box and the brightness habit is one with a sudden drop after a longer or shorter period of initial adjustment. The following records showing the number of errors in successive groups of 10 trials are selected from a series of 30 normal cases trained in brightness discrimination:

```
8  5  7  4  3  5*  1  0  0  0
9  7*  0  0  0
7  5  4*  1  1  1  1  0  0  0
5  5  5  5  6  2  2  5  6*  0  1  0  0  0
6  6  8  9  4  5  3  3  5*  0  0  0
8  6  8  6  3  4*  0  0  0
5  6  5  2  1  3  4  5  5*  0  0  0
5  5  8  7  7  4  6  6  6  2  6*  0  0  0
```

There is in each case a rather sudden drop (*) from a chance number of errors to one or no errors in 10 trials. Sixteen of the 30 records conform to this type; the others show a more continuous decrease in errors. Where it appears, a gradual decrease is likely to be deceptive, for it actually depends, at least in part, upon other factors than discrimination. In the preceding records it will be noted that the majority of animals make more than a chance number of errors (5) in the first days of training. Many animals tend to explore the entire box at every trial until they become thoroughly adapted to the routine of training, and the initial improvement is largely due to this.

Both the doubt-platform box and the discrimination box present situations which are more foreign to the daily activities of the animals than are the mazes. Orientation in a stable environment is a constant phase of the animal's behavior; the situation in the maze may be complex, but it involves no unfamiliar elements. The discrimination and problem-box experiments, on the contrary, require an association between two elements of the situation which have probably never before been identified in the animal's experience.

As an analogous case, a trained mathematician, when confronted with an intricate problem, may proceed directly, by the application of familiar principles, to the solution. He may consume far more time and effort when forced to diagnose ignition trouble and start his stalled car, although the actual principles involved are vastly simpler. He consumes time with this and that experimental adjustment; but once he discovers dirt in the distributor, the habit of turning first to that point is quickly established.

There are many indications that animals in problem-box situations experiment with many solutions. Thus one rat, in experiments with the inclined-plane box (Lashley and Franz, 1917), originally opened the box by an accidental fall from the roof of the restraining cage. For several trials thereafter she systematically climbed to the roof and let go, totaling more than 50 falls before the method was abandoned. Persistence in other less-striking false solutions may be frequently observed. Similarly in the discrimination box, responses to position, to alternation, or to cues from the experimenter's movements usually precede the reactions to the light and represent attempted solutions which are within the rat's customary range of activity.

In both types of habit there is often a specific response to the essential parts of the problem which foreshadows the solution. Thus the animal which has run across the platform many times without pause, stops and explores the platform thoroughly. The door is opened during this exploration, and thereafter all activity in the restraining cage centers about the platform and door. In the discrimination box likewise, a long exploration of the stimulus plate is often followed by a series of correct responses.

The form of the learning curve is the more significant when considered in relation to such behavior. In many cases it strongly suggests that the actual association is formed very quickly and that both the practice preceding and the errors following are irrelevant to the actual formation of the association. The "all-or-nothing" action of the discrimination habit is very apparent in some studies of the threshold of brightness discrimination which are now in progress. When the difference in intensities approaches the animal's limen, he falls back upon position or right-left alternation as a basis of reaction. If now the difference is increased again to the point at which he was discriminating accurately before, he may persist in the position or alternation habit for many trials, then suddenly drop from 50 to 0 per cent error, and this usually corresponds to a change from a slap-dash to a cautious traversing of the discrimination compartment. There is no present way to record such behavior objectively, and I can present the description only as an impression from the training of several hundred animals in these problems. Nevertheless, I believe that the picture will be a familiar one to all who have had experience in training animals in the Yerkes box and that it justifies us in interpreting the discrimination habit as a simple association acquired only after a number of more familiar solutions have been tried unsuccessfully.

The complexity of the maze habit.—The solution of the maze problem, on the contrary, seems to involve a more intricate process which is far from adequately accounted for by our theories of maze learning. Habits like that of the maze—in fact, all learning involving a sequence of manipulative or verbal activities—have most frequently been interpreted as series of chain reflexes. Washburn (1916) calls these "movement systems" and defines them as *"a combination of movements so linked together that the stimulus furnished by the actual performance of certain movements is required to bring about other movements."* There is no direct evidence in proof of the correctness of this analysis of serial habits. The demonstration that the habit is not dependent upon stimulation of exteroceptors (Watson, 1907) and observations upon the effects of changing the length of alleys (Carr and Watson, 1908) have shown that the execution of the habit is internally conditioned. In the absence of further evidence, the assumption of a kinaesthetic-motor chain was justified, but the actual functioning of such a mechanism was not proved. The observations on spinal lesions, mentioned earlier (Lashley and Ball, 1929), seem to reduce the kinaesthetic and motor patterns to the same status as the exteroceptors in the performance of the maze habit. They may be utilized as cues to orientation but are not essential to the correct performance of the habit.

Observations on the behavior of animals with pronounced motor disturbances following spinal or cerebellar injuries emphasize the relative unimportance of the movement system. Animals which have learned the maze before the development of the motor inco-ordinations continue to traverse it, although the manner of progression may be almost completely altered. One drags himself through with his forepaws; another falls at every step but gets through by a series of lunges; a third rolls over completely in making each turn, yet manages to avoid rolling into a cul-de-sac and makes an errorless run. The behavior presents exactly the same problem of direct adaptation of any motor organs to the attainment of a given end, which was outstanding in my earlier observations on the behavior of monkeys after destruction of the precentral gyri (Lashley, 1924a, b). If the customary sequence of movements employed in reaching the food is rendered impossible, another set, not previously used in the habit, and constituting an entirely different motor pattern, may be directly and efficiently substituted without any random activity.

Some observations, which I have not yet been able to put on an objective footing, bear out this interpretation. With a number of normal animals which had learned the Maze III, I made the following test. The wire mesh cover was removed from the maze and starting-compartment, and the entrance to the maze blocked. An animal was then placed in the starting-compartment and kept under observation. Of 20 so tested, 5 pursued the most direct course across the tops of the partitions to the food box, with practically no random exploration, 3 wandered about and reached the food seemingly by chance, and the others dropped into the first alley and followed their customary path. The probability of such a result from chance cannot be computed, but the behavior of the 5 that followed the direct course to the food strongly suggested that they were perfectly oriented with respect to its direction, although they had never before reached it save by the indirect path of the maze. Observations of others upon the shortening of the path through the maze, and on a maze constructed to test this question of direct adaptation, likewise suggest that the rat forms, from the indirect path of the maze, some generalization as to the relative positions of the starting and food boxes.

Evidence of various sorts (Peterson, 1917; Kuo, 1922)

points to the formation of a number of positive associations rather than to the dropping of elements from an initial series. The random character of the animal's acts in the maze is questionable, even when the term is used to mean only, "determined by chance external stimuli." One does not realize the meaning of "random" behavior until he has compared a normal animal with one having extensive cerebral destruction. The normal animal almost never re-enters a cul-de-sac without intervening exploration of other parts of the maze. An animal with severe lesions may repeat a single error as many as two hundred times before passing to other parts of the maze. Such a difference can only mean that the normal animal possesses something like an immediate memory which prevents him from repeating an error just made. Similarly, after the first trial or two the normal animal gives evidence of a general orientation which the operated case is sometimes slow in acquiring.

The available evidence seems to justify the conclusion that the most important features of the maze habit are a generalization of direction from the specific turns of the maze and the development of some central organization by which the sense of general direction can be maintained in spite of great variations of posture and of specific direction in running.

RETARDATION NOT SPECIFIC FOR THE MAZE

There is much in the behavior of the operated animals which make poor records in the maze that is suggestive of a general deterioration, although the evidence is difficult to express in quantitative terms. The mazes used were provided with swinging doors limiting progress to one direction at the starting-compartment and food box. The animals with extensive lesions had great difficulty in negotiating these doors. When any animal failed to push through the door to the food box promptly as he reached it in the first trial, he was given special training with the doors until he would react to them readily. Some of the animals with extensive lesions never learned this and were trained throughout the tests with the doors open.

In feeding, the animals with extensive lesions showed various peculiarities. Some, on reaching the food compartment would eat feces or bits of sawdust, although they disregarded similar objects in the maze. All were less aggressive in competition for food with other animals. Many normal animals quickly acquire the habit of filling mouth and paws with bread as the experimenter lifts them from the food box. Such behavior was exceptional among the more deteriorated animals.

In the home cages the operated animals with larger lesions seemed more oblivious to the presence of others than are normal animals. They built no nests, failed to keep themselves clean and free from parasites, and rarely escaped from the home cages, even when the doors were left open. They adapted to handling as quickly as normals, ceasing to struggle or bite when once grasped; but many of them continued to bite viciously at an approaching hand in the home cage.

Many individual peculiarities of behavior developed, such as always dragging the food dish about the cage before eating, persistent digging at the wooden floor of the starting-boxes, and the like. The whole picture is one of a deterioration rather than of a loss which is specific for the mazes. It seems clear that the problem is less to explain the retardation in the maze than to account for the lack of retardation in the other situations.

Experiments still in progress are giving evidence that with increasing complexity of the discrimination problem a retardation appears after brain lesions which is not evident in the simpler discrimination. Thus, animals were trained to approach a single light and avoid darkness. When this habit was established, a second dim light was introduced and the animals trained to choose the brighter of the two. Data for normal animals and for animals with the visual area destroyed were the following:

	NORMALS		OPERATED	
	Errors	Trials	Errors	Trials
Learning light-darkness discrimination....	49.6	125	40.6	110*
Subsequent learning two-light discrimination.................................	3.8	27.7	10.4	53

* As usual the operated animals are superior to normals in learning this problem.

The experiment further involved tests for threshold of discrimination between two lights. For each new setting of the problem the operated animals required more practice than the normals, although their threshold of discrimination, determined after long training, is not very much higher than that of normals. They require more practice for adaptation to the new and complex situations, although the discrimination involved is far above their limen.

These data seem to bear out our interpretation of the differences between the problems as one of complexity. Learning of the simplest mazes largely escapes from influence of cerebral lesions, as does learning of the light-darkness discrimination. With increasing complexity of either situation the retarding effect of lesions becomes apparent.

I am aware that this implies a reversal of the usual conception of the discrimination and maze habits, tending to interpret the former as learning by the trial-and-error use of various solutions within the animal's ordinary experience and the latter as involving a higher level of integration approaching rational learning, but the evidence from many sources seems to me to justify such an interpretation as being most consistent with the available data. Among the mazes the degree of retardation following brain injury is proportional to the relative difficulty of the mazes for normal animals and to the objective complexity of the problems. It seems not unlikely that the actual associations required for the latch boxes and discrimination habit are simpler than those for the mazes and that the escape of these habits from the influence of brain lesions is the result of their greater simplicity.

The supposition that the differences are all due to variations in the complexity of the functions also accords with other evidence that the degree of isolation and exact anatomical localization is inversely proportional to the complexity of the functions (Monakow, 1914, p. 902). We might therefore interpret the data as indicating that the habits of the latch-box and visual discrimination are simple and capable of performance by isolated mechanisms which can be developed rather readily in various parts of the nervous system; that the maze habits are more complex, are dependent upon the activity of larger amounts of tissue, somewhat in proportion to their individual complexity, and hence are not functionally identified with any particular cerebral area.

The interpretation is not very illuminating but seems preferable to the admission that learning may involve two kinds of nervous activity as strikingly different as those which our data otherwise seem to reveal.

None of the studies of learning or retention of the mazes after cerebral lesions has given the slightest indication that the maze habit is made up of independent associational elements. There was never amnesia for one part of the path with retention of another (except that the habit of manipulating the doors, once acquired, was never lost). It was impossible to discover differences in sensory or motor processes which would correlate with the loci of injury or account for the retardation. The diversities of behavior, such as disorientation, tendencies to perseveration, and the like, corresponded somewhat with the magnitude of lesion but not at all with the locus, and seemed to represent diverse degrees of deterioration rather than specific defects. Taken all together, the evidence opposes the existence of a specific deterioration in the cases with extensive lesions and, I believe, justifies the conclusion that the effect which cerebral lesions produce in the rat resembles more closely a general dementia than any of the more specialized defects such as apraxia or cortical anesthesia in man.

CHAPTER X

COMPARISON OF THE RAT WITH OTHER FORMS

The results which we have obtained in the study of cerebral function in the rat indicate that the more complex functions, divorced from purely sensory or motor processes, are largely carried out in independence of structural differentiation. Specific cortical areas, and association or projection tracts, seem unessential to the performance of such functions, which rather depend upon the total mass of normal tissue. Such a conclusion runs counter to much of the accepted theory of cerebral function, with its emphasis upon definite localization, continuity, and discreteness of reflex arcs. This body of theory has grown up gradually from a multitude of experimental and clinical observations which are by no means consistent among themselves. It is possible that the cerebral functions in the rat are not typical of the mechanisms at work in higher forms; it is also possible that we have overdeveloped the simple reflex hypothesis in an effort to make the intricacies of brain function more comprehensible.

Most of our knowledge of cerebral function is based upon studies of the dog, monkey, and man. I shall review briefly some of the work with these forms, first, to show that the observed facts are not inconsistent with our data for the rat and, second, to indicate the changes which have occurred with increase in complexity of function.

CEREBRAL FUNCTION IN THE DOG

Few facts concerning the effects of cerebral lesions in the dog are clearly established. It is difficult to evaluate the older work, and there has been little attempt to check it since the development of more adequate methods of studying animal behavior. The most extensive studies are those of Goltz (1881), Munk (1909), Hitzig (1903), Luciani and Seppili (1886), Loeb (1884, 1886), Minkowski (1911), Bianchi (1922), and Pavlov (1927). I have not space to review the bitter controversies which characterized the earlier studies. There is scarcely a statement of fact by one which is not denied by others, and there is no agreement as to interpretations.

The visual mechanisms.—Much of the earlier work was concerned with the function of vision and is closely related to our data. There is not conclusive evidence concerning even the peripheral mechanisms of vision in the dog.[1] The dog is probably color blind (Smith, 1912) and lacking in detail vision. Johnson (1916) and Szymanski (1918) were unable to gain any evidence of pattern vision in the dogs which they studied. Pavlov (1927), on the contrary, claims a fair degree of visual acuity and the capacity to distinguish complex visual patterns in the animals studied by Orbeli and Shenger-Krestovnikova. The dog lacks an anatomically demonstrable fovea (Slonaker, 1897); and, since detailed reports of the methods used in Pavlov's laboratory are not available, I am inclined to accept the work of Szymanski and Johnson, pending further analysis of the conditioned-reflex techniques. Most of the attempts to determine the character of vision and the extent of scotoma in work on the visual cortex of the dog have depended upon reaction to movement, either the moving hand of the experimenter or pieces of meat thrown past the animal. We have no controlled study of the normal animal's sensitivity to visual motion and so can make little estimate of the reliability of the observations on animals with brain injuries. In evaluating the experimental studies, we must bear in mind the inadequacy of the methods and the lack of any certain knowledge of vision in the normal animal.

In a long series of studies Munk (1881, 1909) developed his theory of the cortical retina. His conclusions embrace the following points: (1) The entire occipital region of the hemispheres is concerned with vision. (2) Destruction of any area within this region is attended by a local area of permanent blindness ("cortical blindness") corresponding in position to the locus of injury and appearing in the visual field of both eyes, though most extensively in the eye opposite the lesion. (3) The

[1] For a review of experimental work on the behavior of normal dogs, see the paper by Warden and Warner (1928).

area of acute vision is projected on the central portion of the occipital zone (Munk's area A_1). (4) In addition to permanent cortical blindness, lesions within this central zone, if not too extensive, produce "psychic blindness," which is a loss of memory for visual objects and is recoverable. (5) Recovery results from a process of re-education whereby new meanings are attached to visual experience. In addition to these specific associations, the animal learns to disregard the scotomatous areas, as the blind spot is normally disregarded.

Goltz (1881) disputed these results, maintaining that no permanent blindness was ever produced by cerebral lesions, however extensive, and ascribing Munk's results to the "visual weakness" and dementia of the animals.

Luciani and Seppili (1886) repeated much of Munk's work. They confirmed his observations of disturbances of vision from lesions in the occipital region but obtained disturbances also from lesions in other remotely distant areas. The former they considered as true visual disturbances; the latter, as an interference with the associative processes of the visual area. They found bilateral homonymous hemianopia after complete destruction of one parietal, temporal, or occipital area. They were not able to demonstrate any more limited scotomas and claimed, in opposition to Munk, that a partial extirpation of both occipital areas always results in a more or less severe disturbance of vision which is uniform for the entire area of both retinas. They further found that the disturbances of vision are never permanent. Absolute blindness does not result from any cortical lesion, and only partial "psychic blindness" follows extensive occipital lesions (e.g., the animal orients to food but fails to distinguish it from cork).

Loeb (1884, 1886) attacked Munk's work upon still other grounds. He failed to demonstrate complete hemianopia after any unilateral lesion but did obtain homonymous weakness of vision (hemiamblyopia) after such lesions. He denied the representation of the area of acute vision in Munk's area A_1 and claimed, first, that any part of the visual cortex *might* be destroyed without the slightest disturbance of vision and, second, that when disturbances did occur they were always in the form of a complete hemiamblyopia with the best vision in the original macula. He ascribed the temporary defects of vision to shock and denied that they are improved by retraining, citing cases of improvement in animals kept in darkness after operation. Finally, he opposed the conception of "psychic blindness," claiming that Munk's cases for which the loss of associations without blindness was claimed were really cases of extensive hemiamblyopia in which the remaining intact field was so small that the animals could not perceive the whole of the objects to be recognized.

Bernheimer (1900) ascribed "psychic blindness," not to the destruction of area A_1 or any other restricted cortical area. He believed that the projection fibers from the macula are widely distributed to the occipital cortex and that any lesion is likely to interrupt a sufficient number of them to produce visual disturbances.

Hitzig (1903), after a study of more than 100 cases, denied almost all of Munk's findings. There is no accurate projection of the retina on the cortex but only a tendency for representation of the quadrants with a great deal of individual variation. Scotomas are never complete, except perhaps after complete destruction of the occipital lobes, but involve retention of sensitivity to light. Marked reactions to light can frequently be elicited when no response to visual objects appears. There is complete recovery from the effects of the majority of lesions, the partial scotomas lasting only a few days or, at most, weeks. The defects of vision are due to disturbances of perception, not of the associative mechanism, and are not "psychic blindness," in Munk's sense.

Vitzou (1893) reported total permanent blindness after complete extirpation of the occipital lobes in dogs. His descriptions of the lesions are inadequate and he later reported partial recovery of vision in monkeys subjected to the same type of lesion. Bechterew (1911) states that permanent blindness resulted from destruction of the mesial surfaces of the occipital lobes and that lesions to the lateral surfaces produced only temporary symptoms.

The most careful study of the visual area in the dog is that of Minkowski (1911). He finds no permanent disturbance of vision after destruction of the lateral or dorsal convexities of the occipital lobes. Ablation of the mesial surface (the area striata) of one hemisphere produces a permanent blindness which involves the lateral three-fourths of the visual field of the contralateral eye and a temporary disturbance of vision in the nasal fourth of the visual field of the eye of the same side. The upper and lower halves of the visual field are represented in the lower and upper halves of the area striata, respectively.

Complete destruction of both striate areas is followed by complete and permanent blindness, such that even avoiding reactions to bright lights cannot be re-established. The animals show a disturbance of spacial orientation which is far more severe than that reported for peripherally blinded dogs (Johnson, 1913).

Minkowski denies a cell-to-cell correspondence between retina and cortex but believes that "every perceptual element of the retina is in relation with a whole area of perceptual elements in the cortex."

Pavlov (1927) reports only the results of complete extirpation of the occipital cortex. Animals with such lesions lost all visual habits and failed to reacquire any reactions to visual patterns in their ordinary environment. "Neither men nor animals nor food were discriminated by these animals by sight." But it was possible to establish conditioned reflexes to light; to differences in luminous intensity, and, in one case, the discrimination between a luminous cross and circle, under the simpler conditions of the laboratory.

It is difficult to discover the truth in this record of contradictions. Doubtless, differences in method will account for the discrepancies; but none of the methods of examining the visual field were free from interpretative error, and there is little choice with respect to reliability. Minkowski has controlled the extent of lesion most carefully, and his work seems to demonstrate a cortical blindness from destruction of the area striata and a separate representation of the four quadrants of the retina on the occipital cortex. This area is difficult to reach by ordinary operative techniques, and it seems probable that experimenters who report recovery from scotomas have not completely destroyed the visual cortex.

A significant point is that Minkowski obtained either a complete hemianopia in the lateral field, defects involving an entire quadrant, or recoverable symptoms. That is, unless the entire cortical field corresponding to a retinal quadrant is destroyed, the defects do not appear to be permanent. Poppelreuter (1917) has pointed out that in man the variety of form shown by scotomas is less than the probable variety of form in central lesions and that the scotomas for the most part extend along entire quadrants either from the center or from the periphery of the visual field. These facts indicate that in both the dog and man there is some equipotentiality of function within each cortical field representing a quadrant of the retina.

In our experiments with the rat recovery of the capacity for brightness discrimination has appeared after the complete destruction of the area striata; but such evidence as is at hand indicates that recovery is not possible in the absence of the entire cerebral cortex. This suggests that in the rat the cortical representation of the retina is more diffuse than in the dog and perhaps lacks the unilateral differentiation. Any part of the cortex may mediate the visual functions, at least for brightness discrimination, and within the whole area striata the parts are equipotential. In the dog the central representation is more limited, and quadrantal distribution appears, especially in the nasal retina; but within the limits of this specialization, the parts may still be equipotential.

The question of "psychic blindness" in the dog is still unsettled. Munk's theory of localized memory images does not accord with modern views of nervous organization, but the question as to whether visual habits may be permanently lost without actual cortical blindness has not been tested by any of the experimenters. For the rat, our data seem conclusive. Habits are lost as a result of occipital lesion, without loss of sensitivity to the stimulus; are not reacquired spontaneously, at least within a limited time (Lashley, 1926); and are reacquired by retraining. This agrees with the conclusions of Munk as opposed to those of Loeb. The loss of habits is not necessarily due to the destruction of Munk's area A_1 or of any other specific area, nor does it seem to be the result of the interruption of association paths as claimed by Bernheimer and Monakow.

The data for the dog on pattern vision are inconclusive, and there are no comparable experiments for the rat. None of the work on the visual area of the dog bears upon the question of mass function. Hitzig alone has a sufficient number of cases for statistical treatment, but the lesions are so incompletely described that it has been impossible to correlate the extent of injury with the histories of recovery from scotoma which he gives.

The problem of intelligence in the dog.—I have already described the views of Flourens (1842), Goltz (1881), Munk (1909), Loeb (1902), and Bianchi (1922) on the question of the localization of intelligence (pp. 4–9). These views were largely based upon work with dogs. Flourens, Goltz, and Loeb maintained a participation of all parts of the cortex in intelligent behavior without subordinate localization of contributing capacities. Munk denied special centers for intelligence but considered it a function of the summated capacities of the sensory fields. Hitzig and Bianchi argue for special centers serving for the final integration of the lower organization of the sensory fields.

These studies are all impressionistic in character. No attempt was made to express the efficiency of performance of the animals in quantitative terms, and there was rarely any comparison of the effects of lesions in different areas by the same investigator. Serious deterioration has been reported after extensive destructions in all parts of the hemispheres; there is no certain evidence that it is more severe after lesions to one area than to another, and no clear distinction between sensory defects and those of more complex organization. Several investigators

(Goltz, Loeb, Bianchi) have stated that extensive lesions produce more severe disorders of intelligence than do slight, but give little objective evidence for the statement.

Franz (1902) measured the efficiency of performance of motor habits in cats and found loss of habits after frontal lobe lesions. The animals formed the habits again after the lesions, and untrained animals also learned them after the removal of the frontal lobes. Not enough cases were used to give reliable comparisons, but there is no indication that the operated animals learned more slowly than normals.

From studies of the formation of conditioned reflexes in dogs with cerebral lesions Pavlov concludes:

. . . . what our experiments do most emphatically refute is the doctrine of special "association" centers, or, more generally, of the existence in the hemispheres of some special area on which the higher functions of the nervous system depend—a doctrine which has already been strenuously opposed by H. Munk.

In so far as they are reliable, the studies of cerebral function in the Carnivora are not inconsistent with our results on the rat, nor do they indicate that there has been any fundamental change in the character of cerebral organization in these supposedly higher forms.

CEREBRAL FUNCTION IN THE MONKEY

Visual functions.—Visual function in the monkey has been less extensively studied than in the dog. Normal vision is probably not significantly different from that of man (Johnson, 1916a; Watson, 1909). Munk (1909) reported homonymous hemiaopia after removal of one occipital lobe and complete blindness after removal of both. He concluded that the area of acute vision is projected upon the posterolateral surface of the occipital pole. Later investigators have confirmed the general locus of the visual area but have found the symptoms of lesion within the occipital lobes less definite and more evanescent than reported by Munk. Schäfer and Brown (1888) found that blindness occurred after occipital destruction, but that partial recovery of vision took place unless the lesion extended far beyond the anatomical visual area. They found the foveal projection at the anterior end of the calcarine fissure, following their conception of its localization in man.

Vitzou (1897, 1898) found blindness subsequent to destruction of the occipital lobes with recovery of ability to recognize objects by sight after 2–21 months. This recovery he ascribed, on insufficient evidence, to regeneration of nervous tissue (1897). Panici (1903) obtained demonstrable visual defects only on complete extirpation of the occipital lobe, and permanent defects only after destruction of all the cortex caudad to the fissure of Rolando. Neither of these authors give an adequate description of the tests of vision employed or of the character of the lesions.

Bechterew (1911) concludes on the basis of work done in his laboratory that the visual projection is to the lateral surfaces of occipital lobes. Franz (1911), on the other hand, found no true visual defects after destruction of the lateral occipital areas. In one animal, in which most of the areas surrounding the calcarine fissure were destroyed, visual defects developed, but not until several days after the operation. This animal was not kept long enough for a study of recovery.

From these experiments it is not possible to form any adequate conception of the functions of the visual areas in the monkey. Apparently visual defects of hemiamblyopic character develop after extensive lesions in one occipital lobe if the mesial surface is involved, but there is a partial recovery and never complete blindness unless the entire cortex caudad to the fissure of Rolando is removed. The tests of vision have in no case been complete and varied enough to give a clue to the nature of the partial defects, beyond the rough delimitation of scotomatous areas. There is no evidence to show whether or not any scotoma involving less than half of the visual field is produced by small lesions.

The problem of intelligence.—Only two serious attempts have been made to estimate the intelligence of monkeys with cerebral lesions. I have already cited the work of Bianchi (1922) as indicating a general deterioration following frontal lesions but failing to control this result with studies of other areas. Franz (1907) reports the loss of habits as a result of frontal lesions with their subsequent reacquisition at, probably, a normal rate: that is, with no evidence of loss of ability to learn as a result of frontal lesions.

The available evidence is inadequate to show either the association of intelligent behavior with any particular part of the cortex or its dependence upon the extent of the lesions.

CORRESPONDENCES AND DIFFERENCE IN CEREBRAL FUNCTION IN THE RAT AND MAN

The trend of much recent literature dealing with symptoms of brain injury in man is away from the doctrines of definite localization of higher functions and toward a psychological rather than an anatomical interpretation of the data. For the simplest sensory processes the evidence for precision and detail of localization has perhaps increased in recent years (Holmes and Lister, 1916; Marie and Chatelin, 1914–15; Piéron, 1923), but for all the integrative functions of the cortex the evidence is more and more opposed to the conception of a mosaic distribution of capacities. Even for the exact localization of the simplest processes the evidence is not altogether convincing.

There are several considerations which must make us wary of accepting clinical literature at its face value. Clinical methods for examining behavior have been notoriously defective. In the older literature, which still forms the foundation for our conceptions of cerebral function, one rarely finds a statement of what the patient can do in any field of activity. Rather there is a pigeonholing in some one of the formal categories, as transcortical aphasia, which are logical rather than empirical. In the whole literature of neurology there is scarcely an attempt to measure the actual capacity of a patient with brain injury to perform such a varied assortment of tasks as is included in a modern intelligence test. The statement that patients may suffer loss of specific capacities as a result of brain injury without some general intellectual disturbance thus lacks any adequate proof.

The anatomical studies are in a scarcely better case than those of behavior. I know of no attempt in the whole literature of neurology to determine what proportion of any anatomical area was destroyed by a lesion; and in many cases which are cited as evidence on the localization question, the delimitation of the lesions is woefully inexact. In recent studies, where exact methods of measuring behavior have been introduced, it has for the most part been impossible to determine the exact position of the lesions because of the survival of the patients.

A third defect is one of logical method. The evidence for separate localization of two functions is always nothing more than the survival of one after a lesion which abolished the other. The possibility of a relationship between cerebral mass or mass of a functional area and the complexity of the acts possible casts doubt upon this fundamental assumption of the doctrine of localization. It may be that color-vision, spacial localization within the visual field, perception of depth, and other complex visual functions which are abolished independently of cortical blindness may have a separate localization on the cortex; but such evidence does not establish the fact, for there is also the possibility that they may be functions of the same area working at a more complex level of integration, which is disturbed by a smaller lesion than are the more primitive functions, just as the habit for Maze III is disturbed by lesions which leave the habit for Maze I unaffected.

Where capacities to react to the spacial distribution of the elements of the stimulus are involved, as in visual or tactile sensitivity, there is evidence for a more or less complete spacial representation of the sensory surface upon the cerebral cortex; but where such spacial relationships are not involved, there is no evidence for a minute differentiation of functional localization.

I shall not attempt to review here the recent clinical findings which support this view but shall only cite a few studies which represent the most thorough that have been made with clinical material and which conform in many ways to the results with the rat. Klüver (1927) has recently summarized the studies of the visual function in relation to the occipital cortex. The evidence is conflicting but in general emphasizes the functional complexity of visual perception and the impossibility of reducing it to any simple capacities which may be separately localized. The same non-additive character of cerebral functions appears in the observations on disturbances of vision by Poppelreuter (1917), Fuchs (1920), Gelb and Goldstein (1920), and in the studies of aphasia by Marie (1906), Moutier (1908), Pick (1913), Monakow (1905, 1914), and Head (1926). However great their contradictions on matters of detail, all point to the essentially unitary character of apparently complex cortical functions and the impossibility of expressing them adequately either as mosaic patterns or as aggregations of cerebral reflexes.

Loss of specific functions appears and is associated with definitely localized lesions, but the functions lost partake more of the nature of intelligence than of the wholly specialized character which it has been customary to ascribe to them. They are global, in the sense of Marie; and although they do not involve equally all aspects of behavior, they do represent functions which may participate in a great variety of activities. Head (1926) stresses the fact that the aphasias are not purely disturbances in the use of language but include disorders of thinking which find expression both in verbal and in all other forms of symbolic expression.

Any form of mental behaviour is liable to suffer which demands reproduction and use of any symbol between its initiation and fulfilment. I do not believe that it is possible to include within one categorical definition all those activities which experience shows to be affected; and yet, from a physiological point of view they form a group of defects as definite as those of sensation.

Again,

It is impossible to find any single term to include all these disorders of behaviour, which extend on the one hand from mechanical aptitudes to exercises in formal logic on the other.

From a detailed examination of a case of verbal aphasia Bouman and Grünbaum (1925) conclude,

Through all his behavior the same type of defect could be traced. This is characterized by a stopping of psychic or psychomotor processes at a primitive phase of normal development on the way from an amorphous total impression to a differential unfolding.

More explicitly,

> The patient is not able to hold in mind the concrete elements of a problem and at the same time manipulate them in thought.

Goldstein (1924), basing his conclusions on studies of both visual and aphasic defects, concludes that, although isolated disturbances of simple sensory or motor functions may occur, in any disturbance of the higher functions, there is always a greater or lesser involvement of the entire cortical organization.

The relation of these conclusions to the problem of intelligence is not wholly clear. Head denies that intelligence is specifically affected in aphasia, except in so far as it is dependent upon the use of symbols.

> It is not the "general intellectual capacity" which is primarily affected, but the mechanism by which certain aspects of mental activity are brought into play. . . . . Behaviour suffers in a specific manner: an action can be carried out in one way but not in another. In so far as these processes are necessary for the perfect exercise of mental aptitudes, "general intelligence" undoubtedly suffers.

Moutier, Bouman and Grünbaum, and Goldstein, on the contrary, stress the global nature of the disturbances and the involvement in aphasia of functions which are allied to, or a part of, general intelligence.

Whatever the final outcome of this problem, it is evident that the most careful recent studies of cerebral function in man are in the main not opposed to our results with the rat. In the former there is a greater specialization, but within the specialized areas there is every indication of a lack of specificity such as we have seen for the whole cortex and the maze habits in the rat. This non-additive character of complex functions is expressed by Head (1926) as follows:

> No function is "localized" strictly in any part of the cortex and no form of activity, somatic or psychical, is built up into a mosaic of elementary processes which become evident when it is disturbed by a lesion of the brain.
>
> On the other hand local destruction of tissue prevents the normal fulfilment of some form of behaviour and the reaction which follows expresses the response of the organism as a whole under these changed conditions.

Moreover, the abnormal manifestations can be described only in terms of the act which has been disturbed, and do not reveal the supposed elements out of which it has been synthesised.

Further, it is at least an open question whether or not the highest co-ordinations in man are not a function of the entire cortex and influenced by lesions within any area. Head almost alone has attempted to measure the abilities of his patients. His results oppose the non-specificity of the cortex, but his methods of measurement are by no means adequate to reveal any but gross defects of general intelligence, if this should exist as a separate function. His protocols certainly indicate that some defect of intelligence is always involved in the specific disorders. Whether we say that this defect is primary or secondary depends largely on whether our preconceptions involve the notion of intelligence as an aggregate or as a general factor.

For the problem of mass relationships the clinical literature is of little value, for it includes quantitative data on neither the extent of destruction nor the degree of deterioration. Nevertheless, there are numerous hints of such a relationship in the grosser estimates of behavior. Small lesions, even within sensory areas, are unattended by symptoms. Bianchi (1922) concludes that marked intellectual disturbance after frontal lesions occurs only if the greater part of the frontal lobes is involved, which implies both a mass relationship and an equipotentiality of parts within this area. Monakow (1914) likewise holds that dementia follows only extensive or diffuse degeneration of the cortex. Head says,

The deeper and wider, therefore, the injury to the cortex and underlying structures, the graver and more permanent is likely to be the loss of function; but we must never forget that it has disturbed a highly organized act and has not removed a strictly definable anatomical "center."

Goldstein (1923) mentions that with the assumption of the function of an entire area by a part of it (in pseudofovea) there is usually a general reduction in the functional level of efficiency.

Our data on the relation of the complexity of the problem to extent of lesion and difficulty find parallels in the clinical literature. Bouman and Grünbaum consider the aphasias as an indication of cerebral functioning at a lower level of complexity. Goldstein (1924) similarly defines "amnestic aphasia." Head states,

> The dependence of the manifest defects on the intellectual difficulty of the act to be performed is one of the most important factors in the problem of aphasia. For it is obvious that any disturbance of symbolic formulation and expression must be looked for and can be discovered soonest, in those tasks which require the greatest expenditure of mental effort in this direction. Thus, since it is harder to carry out a test which offers three possibilities of an erroneous answer, than one which demands a single choice, the former is the first to suffer and is most severely affected throughout the course of the disorder.

A similar conclusion is drawn by Heidenhain (1927), who finds that the recognition of visual material by subjects with occipital lesions is limited by the complexity of the material.

This brief summary of literature on other forms than the rat shows the similarity of problems which arise at all levels of complexity and the narrow limitations of our actual knowledge of cerebral mechanisms. Specialization of function of different parts of the cortex occurs in all forms, but at best this is only a gross affair, involving general categories of activity rather than specific reactions. The more complicated and difficult the activity, the less the evidence for its limitation to any single part of the nervous system, and the less the likelihood of its disintegration into subordinate physiological elements.

The statement is often made, chiefly from studies of the excitability of the motor cortex, that with ascent in the evolutionary scale there is an increasing specialization and fineness of localization within the cerebral cortex. In one respect only does the evidence corroborate this: in the mammalian series the higher forms have a greater capacity to discriminate differences in the spacial distribution of stimuli on sensory surfaces (skin, retina, organ of Corti) and a greater independence of control of motor segments. Corresponding to this increased capacity for spacial adjustments, there is a finer differentiation within the sensory and motor projection fields of the cortex. But, aside from this function of spacial orientation, there is little evidence of a finer cortical differentiation in man than in the rat.

CHAPTER XI

NEURAL MECHANISMS IN ADAPTIVE BEHAVIOR

The direct evidence on cerebral organization in the rat and also many results from brain lesions in higher forms indicate that there is a correspondence of structural and functional differentiation only between the grosser units of anatomy and behavior. Some functions are conditioned only by the cortex as a whole and suffer qualitatively similar defects after destruction of the most diverse cortical fields. Others suffer only after lesions within particular areas, but do not show qualitatively diverse effects from diverse lesions within the functional areas. Restricted lesions result in a reduction of efficiency in a wide range of performance, and there is a definite limit to the possible dissociation of functions.

The hypothesis of restricted conduction-paths might be elaborated to account for such global effects by the assumption that each activity is mediated by a multiplicity of equivalent arcs traversing different parts of the cortex and contributing to functional efficiency by mutual facilitation. The evidence presented on pages 129–31 is opposed to such an interpretation, however, and, since the assumption of equivalent arcs is inadequate to account for other instances of independence of structure (see below), the assumption is not justified.

The whole implication of the data is that the "higher level" integrations are not dependent upon localized structural differentiations but are a function of some more general, dynamic organization of the entire cerebral system. This conclusion is borne out by evidence from other sources. In the analysis of the adequate stimulus to many activities we find a condition which seems incompatible with any theory of the determination of reaction through localized structure. In the spinal reflex the excitation of a single end-organ or small group of end-organs elicits a reaction which may be specific for that group of sensory endings, so that, in some cases, it seems possible to establish a point-for-point correspondence between afferent and efferent fibers, as in the scratch reflex. But this is true, if ever, only in the case of the simplest reflexes of the spinal animal. When we turn to activities which we designate as "behavior," we are unable to establish a similar correspondence.

Under the influence of the reflex theory I attempted, some years ago, an analysis of the instinctive recognition of their young by birds (Lashley, 1915) in the hope of being able to determine the particular receptor cells and reflex arcs whose excitation aroused the responses. It was speedily clear that the adequate stimulus could not be expressed in any such terms but was a pattern which might vary widely in detail and in the end-organs stimulated. Similar studies of the sex behavior of the rat (Stone, 1922, 1923) and unpublished work on recognition of the young in the rat and the nursing reactions of kittens indicate clearly that the essential element of the stimulus is not the excitation of a pattern of specific sensory endings but the excitation of any endings in a particular spacial or temporal pattern. A review of the literature on instinct seems to me to suggest that the characteristic of instinctive behavior as distinct from reflexes is just this capacity to be aroused by a pattern of excitation, irrespective of the particular afferent cells which conduct the stimulus.

The problem is most clearly exemplified in human pattern vision. With the eye fixed and a pattern moved across the field of the macula, the same reaction (e.g., naming the object) may be elicited at any one of a thousand points, no two of which involve excitation of exactly the same retinal cells. To say that a specific habit has been formed for each of the possible positions is preposterous, for the pattern may be one never before experienced. The alternative is that the response is determined by the proportions of the pattern and, within the limits of visual acuity, is independent of the particular cells excited.

This means that, not only on the retina, but also in the central projection on the cortex, there is a constant flux of stimulation such that the same cells are rarely, if ever, twice excited by the same stimulus, yet a constant reaction is produced. The activity of the visual cortex must resemble that of one of the electric signs in which a pattern of letters passes rapidly across a stationary group of lamps. The structural pattern is fixed, but the functional pattern plays over it without limitation to specific elements.

Examples of this type of adequate stimulation are easier to find than exceptions. Weber's circles are the most familiar, but all visual and tactual recognition of objects seems to be of the same character. Temporal patterns as well as spacial must be admitted, as in the recognition of a melody played at different tempos or in different keys. We seem forced to the conclusion that the final common path may be sensitized to such patterns, so that a constant reaction is given to them, no matter in what part of a cortical field they occur.

Turning to the motor reactions themselves, we find a closely analogous condition in the functional equivalence of responses, where various motor organs may be used interchangeably to produce the same end-result. Perhaps the most primitive instance of this sort is the innervation of supernumerary limbs reported by Weiss (1924) and by Detweiler (1922 and 1925). I have reported cases of direct substitution of unpracticed limbs in the solution of problem boxes by monkeys (Lashley, 1924a). A familiar example is the capacity to form letters of an unaccustomed size without special practice for each new combination of movements. The most striking instance of the sort that has come to my attention is that of a student of piano who, in the stress of a public recital, unknowingly transposed one-half tone upward an entire movement of a Beethoven sonata, a feat which she had never attempted before and could not duplicate afterward even with some practice.

In such cases of equivalence of response it seems that almost any effector organ may be utilized in the performance of functionally equivalent movements. We know nothing of the mechanism by which the equivalence is initially established, but it is unquestionable that, once it is established, the substitution may occur in a new situation without the formation of new habits specific for that situation(e.g., the grammatical use of a newly acquired word in entirely new settings).

It seems clear that there can be no specific connections of the various available motor organs with the central mechanism which mediates the habit. In one of my cases the left arm was paralyzed throughout the training of the right in a series of complicated manipulative movements. There was thus no opportunity for direct integration of the final common path of the left arm with the neural organization of the habit. Yet, on recovery from paralysis, the arm performed the correct movements without practice. Such instances force the conclusion that the impulses to activity arising in the higher centers are not specific excitations of particular muscles but rather in the nature of a generalized impulse to movement in relation to the orientation of the body, which may control equally well the movements of diverse limbs.

The phenomena of sensory recognition of ratios, of direct adaptation of unpracticed motor organs, and of central equipotentiality and mass function seem to me to represent, at a simple level, the same problem which in more intricate form is proposed by intelligent acts. In so far as we can define them, "intelligent acts" are those dealing with relationships rather than with concrete units. Insight consists of the identification of two systems of elements through common relationships among their parts. It is, I think, certain that these relationships are not patterns of identical elements, but are, rather, similar relations subsisting among dissimilar elements. There is no possibility of reducing association by similarity to the excitation of the same synapses or reflex arcs. A theorem applied to the solution of a problem in geometry may differ in every detail from the statement of the problem and yet be immediately associated because of common spacial relations involved.

Neurologically these relationships must be in the nature of ratios of excitation, patterns without a fixed anatomical substratum, since the sensory and motor elements of a situation may change fundamentally without altering its logical significance. We seem forced to the conclusion that a final common path may somehow be sensitized to a pattern of excitation so that it will respond to this pattern in whatsoever part of the nervous tissue it may occur. In the simplest cases the relationships forming the basis of reaction seem expressible as ratios of intensity of excitation; in others, as ratios of spacial extent or temporal distribution. The relationships involved in insight are more difficult to analyze, but there is in some instances sufficient similarity to cases of sensory discrimination to suggest that the basic mechanism must be fundamentally the same.

The problem of reaction to ratio thus seems to underlie all phases of behavior, to such a degree that we might be justified in saying that the unit of neural organization is not the reflex arc or the system of reciprocal innervation (Brown, 1914) but is the mechanism, whatever be its nature, by which reaction to a ratio is produced. The question raised here has not been considered adequately in theories of neural organization, and the current doctrines seem wholly unsuited to deal with it.

THEORIES OF CEREBRAL LOCALIZATION NOT EXPLANATORY

The facts of localization of function, although of considerable clinical importance in the location of tumors and the like, have been of little value for an understanding of the mechanisms of the brain. As psychologists we are interested in such problems as how the isolated elements of speech, the separate tongue, laryngeal, and respiratory movements are integrated in language; how grammatical form arises and words fall into the linguistic mold; how memories are registered and recalled; how a constantly varying visual object may arouse a constant reaction; how intelligence solves its problems. For these and like questions it is scarcely helpful to know that isolated movements may be elicited by stimulation of the precentral gyrus, that the faculty of speech is or is not localized in Brocca's area or Marie's quadrilateral, that fibers of the macula are projected upon the occipital pole, that intelligence suffers from lesions to the frontal lobes. If it were shown conclusively that grammatical form is the exclusive function of a particular area, that point-for-point correspondence of cortex and retina involves also a point-for-point correspondence of cortex and effector cells, as Loeb has claimed (1912), that lesions to postfrontal areas do not affect intelligence, there might be a significant basis for understanding of the mechanisms, in so far as we might seek in these areas a differential structural basis for the functions; but for all such critical questions the evidence either has been inconclusive or has opposed the more simple and comprehensible interpretation.

Localized lesions produce symptoms which vary with the area involved, but the character of these symptoms is such as to preclude anatomical correlations significant for the problem of brain mechanisms. Localization as an explanatory principle can progress in only one way; by the demonstration of correspondences between ever more restricted anatomical divisions and smaller units of behavior until some ultimate anatomical and behavioristic elements are reached—the old notion of elementary ideas located in single cells of the brain. But this is clearly not the principle of neural organization. When a defect occurs from cerebral injury, it involves a whole constellation of activities. There is not a loss of a few specific associations, an amnesia for a few words and not for others; rather there is the loss of a mode of thinking or acting, and all processes belonging to the class are equally affected (for example, grammatical form without regard to specific verbal content). Further, the symptoms usually appear not as an absolute loss of function but as a greater or lesser difficulty of performance. Thus hemiplegia may improve temporarily under emotional excitement (Minkowski, 1917; Lashley, 1924a), and capacities for speech in aphasia may vary from time to time (Franz, 1915a) and with the total setting or the temporary condition of facilitation (Head, 1926).

Except for the sensory and motor projection fields, where a spacial distribution corresponds to the surface area of the receptor or effector mechanism, there is little evidence for specialization within the grosser structural areas. Where a fractioning of function within such an area appears, it seems probable that this represents progressive stages in the complexity or organization of the entire field rather than a differential functioning of different areas. Thus the various defects of color, form, and pattern vision have no established connection with different parts of the visual cortex but seem rather to represent different degrees of disorganization within the same mechanism. This is indicated, for example, by the successive steps in recovery from hemianopia recorded by Poppelreuter (1923).

At every turn in the analysis of cerebral localization of function we seem confronted by a problem similar to that of maze learning in the rat. A complex function shows a decrease in efficiency in every part, and this is, at least to some extent, proportional to the magnitude of the lesion and is independent of its locus within a rather wide area. The facts of localization give us no clue to the cerebral mechanisms responsible for such a condition.

THE REFLEX THEORY INADEQUATE

The theory of the reflex was evolved to account for the most unintelligent of behavior, the activities of the "spinal" animal. It was first elaborated in the doctrine of chain reflexes (Spencer) as an explanation of instinct, at a time when no single instinct had been subjected to really critical analysis. More recently and still more uncritically it has been promulgated by the Russian objective school as an adequate basis for explanation of all behavior. The theory has the advantage of simplicity which makes for its popularity as a slogan; but when one is confronted with the necessity of accounting for a particular group of activities, above the level of the spinal reflexes, in terms of the reflex theory and of working out that account in detail, the inadequacy of the theory becomes evident.[1]

The chief difficulty is its implication of a point-for-point correspondence in the relations of receptors, nerve cells, and effectors. Not that this is always expressed; but the comprehensibility and explanatory value of the reflex-arc hypothesis lies in just this definiteness of connections, which permits the tracing of nerve impulses over predetermined paths. Omit this element of restricted paths and the theory becomes nothing more than an assertion of uniformity in the sequence of stimulus and response. Yet it is this very definiteness which is most difficult to har-

---

[1] I am coming to doubt the validity of the reflex-arc hypothesis, even as applied to spinal reflexes. There are many indications that the spinal reflexes are no more dependent upon isolated conduction paths than are cerebral functions.

monize with the problems of psychology and in particular with the behavior which we class as "intelligent." The distinguishing feature of the reactions which we designate as "behavior" in contradistinction to reflex is that they are not conditioned by the excitation of specific limited receptors or by stereotyped central mechanisms but involve features of plasticity which have never been expressed in terms of the reflex theory and which imply, as we have seen, an independence of specifically differentiated conduction paths.

DYNAMIC THEORIES

The fluctuations of function in the cerebral paralyses and the aphasias, giving the impression of variation in the ease of performance of the activities involved, the dependence of learning of certain types, of retention, and of efficiency of performance upon cerebral mass, and the normal fluctuations in efficiency with changes of tonus and of general health point to some non-specific quantitative element in cerebral function which contributes to the facility of performance without determining the particular pattern of integration. The problem has been expressed by the statement that the energy available for the reactions may be inadequate although the nervous patterns of integration are retained. The older neurological literature is filled with references to "nervous energy," as the psychological is with "mental energy"; but few attempts were made to understand its nature.

One of the earlier theories, and by far the most elaborate one, on the nature of nervous energy is that of McDougall (1903). He postulated a special kind of energy (neurin) associated with the activity of the nervous system, capable of storage in reserve, of drainage through open synapses, and of diversion into any one of a number of channels to facilitate various activities. The theory has much to recommend it as an interpretation of psychological data but seems flatly contradicted by more recent data upon the nature of the propagated disturbance in the nerve fiber.

Ebbecke (1919) has developed a theory of nervous energy based upon the assumption of a capacity of nerve and body cells to maintain an excitation imposed upon them and to determine the general level of nervous excitation by a process of irradiation.

Piéron (1923) stresses two possible mechanisms by which local injuries may produce general symptoms independent of the site of the injury. He considers the more important of these to be general interference with the metabolism of the neurons such that their energy of discharge or their capacity to recover from fatigue is reduced. He recognizes also the possibility of a direct reduction of nervous energy by a restricted lesion, in that complex mental operations involve a multiplicity of elements in all parts of the brain, having diverse functions but contributing to the efficiency of the total operation, and the destruction of any of these may reduce the number of mechanisms available for the whole process; but he regards this as a relatively minor factor in the production of general symptoms.

Our data do not accord well with either of these alternatives. In the first place, we have seen that the reduction in capacity for learning subsequent to extensive lesions is permanent, and there is no reason to believe that the metabolism of cells remote from a lesion can be permanently affected by the lesion.[2] The failure to discover qualitative diversities in learning corresponding to diverse loci of injury is likewise difficult to harmonize with the theory that reduction of efficiency is due to the dropping-out of some elements from a complex series.

Head's conception of "vigilance" (1923) represents a formulation of the problem similar to that of Piéron. He points out the simplification of behavior in trauma, anesthesia, and the like. Under the influence of chloroform the automatic centers "do not cease entirely to function, but the vigilance necessary for the

[2] In cases which have survived operation for several months, the cortex, even at the edge of the lesion, is often perfectly normal in appearance, without evidence of shrinkage or changes in cellular appearance. I have often been impressed by the absence of general symptoms where metabolic disturbance is most to be expected. Thus, in an animal which died during a recent experiment, the entire right hemisphere was found to have been replaced by a purulent cyst, and the left was so softened as to be removed with difficulty from the cranium; yet on the day of his death this animal made a perfect record in a difficult discrimination problem.

performance of their high-grade activities has been abolished by the fall of neural potency." Head nowhere defines or attempts an explanation of differences in "neural potency," which is the critical point in his theory, nor does he seek to show how a localized lesion can modify vigilance, so that, for an understanding of our problem, the concept seems rather sterile.

The doctrines of nervous energy, as derived by analogy with forms of physical energy, seem precluded by what we know of the nature of nerve conduction. If, as seems probable from studies of the refractory period of nerve, the response of the neuron is momentary and is followed by a quick return to the resting state after every excitation, there can be no general fund of nervous energy capable of accumulation and diversion into various activities. Adrian (1923) has pointed out the limitations to theories of nervous energy which are set by the "all-or-nothing" law, and his arguments seem conclusive. Nevertheless, so many facts of behavior point to some more general dynamic organization that we cannot escape the problem. Pike (1918) has sketched a theory, based upon the number of fibers excited, which seeks to avoid the difficulty raised by the "all-or-nothing" law; but he does not elaborate the hypothesis sufficiently to permit its application to special problems of cortical facilitation.

Theories of nervous energy are in general opposed to theories of localization. They fit better the facts of plasticity of nervous function, but are of little help for an understanding of specific integrations. Reflex theories deal more adequately with the latter but provide no insight into the mechanisms producing the less stereotyped forms of behavior. None of the existing theories can be applied helpfully to our problems of mass function or equivalence in the sensory and motor fields.

SUGGESTIONS TOWARD A THEORY OF NEURAL ORGANIZATION

The facts which give the chief difficulty to the existing theories may be grouped into four categories: (1) the determination of reactions by patterns or ratios of excitation imposed upon varying anatomical elements (with this must be included the equipotentiality of cerebral areas and association tracts); (2)

the apparent disturbances of equilibrium among the parts of the central nervous system without specific losses of function, as in the occurrence of more-pronounced symptoms from unilateral lesions to the cerebellum, corpus striatum, etc., than from bilateral lesions; (3) the dependence of efficiency in learning and retention and, less certainly, of ease of performance upon the quantity of functional tissue; and (4) the seeming limitation of the possible complexity of organization by the total quantity of nervous tissue. These phenomena all point to a functional organization independent of differentiated structure and to some more-general energy relations within the central nervous system. Whether they are all expressions of some common fundamental mechanism or indications of diverse processes is not yet clear, but the former seems probable since we can find analogous problems in organic behavior at various levels.

In the processes of growth and regeneration we meet the same problems of determination of specific reactions (differentiation) by the interrelations of parts and by the total mass of tissue, the establishment of equilibrated systems, and the limitation of complexity of differentiation by the mass of tissue. The parallel is so close that, I believe, we may turn to the phenomena of morphogenesis for a clue to neural organization.

The mystery of equipotential systems and of self-differentiation in development has been somewhat cleared up by the discovery of axial polarization and the action of physiological gradients in determining the details of growth.

The importance of gradient systems in the control of growth and integration of the nervous system during embryonal life has been brought out by the studies of Kappers (1917) and Child (1924). The course of development seems to involve an ever increasing complexity of interacting gradient systems, becoming more delicately balanced and plastic with each step in structural differentiation. It would be strange if these mechanisms, which contribute so largely to structural organization, should cease to function with the completion of gross development. Rather we should expect to find them assuming a rôle of greatest importance in co-ordinating the activities of the matured organism. Direct experimental evidence of their existence and function in nervous integration is lacking, but the many similarities of the problems of morphogenesis and behavior must incline us to seek a common solution.

The problem of reaction to relations seems to resolve into that of the responsiveness of the final common path to ratios of excitation or to a gradient of excitation between two or more adjacent neurological fields. A differential response to the relative positions of two visual stimuli of unequal intensity, seen at varying distances and with varying points of fixation, will serve as a relatively simple illustration. For such a case we can postulate a mechanism which will meet the necessary conditions for reaction to ratio of excitation without dependence upon particular cellular connections. For this we must make the following assumptions: (1) The excitation of a center results in the establishment of a potential difference between that center and other neural aggregates. This assumption has already been recognized as probable in the widely accepted theory of neurobiotaxis (Kappers, 1917). (2) The excitation of a nerve cell is conditioned by the intensity or direction of current in the electric field within which it lies. We know that metabolic rate, growth, and motility are influenced in this way, and we have reason to believe that excitability is a function of the permeability of membranes upon which the rate of metabolism also depends. (3) The spacial distribution of potential differences within the nervous system corresponds somewhat to the distribution of excitation upon the receptor surfaces. The medullation of the fibers involved in more finely integrated activities provides an insulation (Kappers) against the spread of current except at certain crucial surfaces where medullation is absent, as in the cerebral cortex.

Applying these postulates to the problem of a discrimination reaction, we may assume that a given ratio of stimulus intensities on two peripheral points establishes a potential difference between two corresponding points in the cortex. The direction of polarization and the steepness of gradient will remain constant in spite of considerable alterations in the absolute positions of the centers of excitation. Cells subject to the influence of this system will have their excitability modified in a constant direction so long as the properties of the gradient field are constant.

The point is developed in closer application to the problem in Figure 33. R and L represent final common paths mediating a turn to the right or left, respectively. S is a source of general

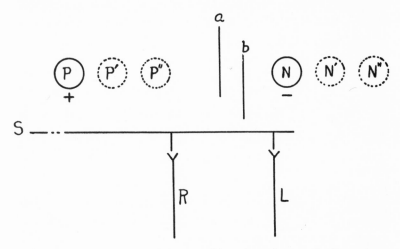

FIG. 33.—Diagram to illustrate the problem of reaction to ratio. For explanation, see text.

excitation aroused by the problem situation and capable of exciting either R or L. P, P', P'' represent variable positions of an area of maximal excitation aroused by one element of the visual pair to be discriminated; and N, N', N'', corresponding positions of a center of lesser excitation aroused by the other. The polarization of the field arising from the difference in potential of P and N remains essentially the same with respect to R and L whether the maximal excitation occurs at $P, P,''$ or any intervening point, and is unaltered by the partial blocking of the intervening conducting tissue at a or b. If the excitability of R and L is modified by any property of the field which differs for their two positions, the field, intensified by the reciprocal relations of the pair, may cause the activation by S of one and not the other, and thus a reaction to the relative position and intensity of the stimuli. Reversal of the relative intensities of the stimuli will reverse the potential difference of P and N and result in the activation of the other member of the reciprocal pair.

There are many objections to the hypothesis in this form. It implies a simple spacial distribution of potential differences which is difficult to harmonize with the structural complexity of the cortex. It does not take into adequate account the facts of conduction in medullated nerve fibers. It gives, in itself, no clue to the nature of more complex patterns. It is unsubstantiated by any direct evidence.

In reply to these objections it may be pointed out that the arrangement of the gray matter is such as to favor the action of a mechanism like that postulated. The structures to which we ascribe the function of integration are generally arranged in thin sheets widely separated. Within these the neurons are unprotected by medullary sheaths and are therefore more susceptible to diffuse chemical or physical agents. The theories of integration by the temporal distribution of nerve impulses assume variations in permeability as one factor in inhibition and facilitation, and this hypothesis assumes only an additional diffuse factor conditioning this permeability. These, of course, are *post hoc* arguments and show only that the hypothesis is not precluded by such facts.

It is possible to elaborate the hypothesis to deal with more complex problems. The relation between efficiency of performance and mass of tissue implies some sort of general facilitation. There is some indication that activation of a habit involves also a partial activation or increase in central tonus of all closely related habit-systems, with the possibility of mutual facilitation and the determination of the general level of activity by the total mass of excitation. The concept involved here is similar to that which I have developed in greater detail in relation to the functions of the precentral gyrus (Lashley, 1924a).

The limitation of complexity of behavior by the quantity of tissue finds a parallel in cases of regeneration of radial forms

(Hydra), where the number of regenerated segments is determined by the size of the regenerating piece. This suggests that the number of co-existing potential fields may somehow be limited by the total mass; and, although it does not reveal the mechanism, it brings our data on the relation of the extent of lesion to the complexity of the problems learned into relation with the general hypothesis.

To deal with specific problems of complex behavior, many phases of neural function must be considered: the elaborate organization of postural reflexes, the partial activation of reaction systems making possible differential timing of actions, the interplay of rhythmic activities, the relations of emotional facilitation to emphasis and the temporal ordering of reactions, as well as the possibility of complex patterns of potential differences (such as can be demonstrated in the growing embryo). By appealing to mechanisms of this sort, it is possible to give a sketchy but fairly plausible account of even such complex processes as the determination of grammatical form, but it is likewise futile until we have clearer evidence concerning the fundamental assumptions.

I have not suggested this hypothesis as a picture of the actual processes in the central nervous system but only as an illustration of the direction in which the facts of neural plasticity seem to force our speculations. There is as yet no clue to the nature of the dynamic forces in nervous activity. It seems impossible to deal with them solely in terms of the propagated disturbances in nerve fibers; but their action may be electrical or electrochemical, diffuse or conducted through the nervous network, continuous or intermittent. They may act as an accessory to the anatomically restricted reflex functions, modifying the conductivity for nerve impulses; or they may constitute the sole basis of nervous integration, giving the illusion of definiteness of structural connection where the conditions of their activity are simple.

Once we recognize the pressing need for an investigation in this direction, it should not be difficult to devise methods for testing the validity of such hypotheses, through the application of electrical measuring devices, chemical indicators, and the like. At present it seems fairly certain only that the facts of plasticity of behavior compel the assumption of such forces, independent of pre-established conduction paths, and showing some, at least, of the properties of gradient systems.

It is obvious that the view of nervous functioning presented here does not give us the simple lucid explanations possible with the reflex hypothesis. But this lucidity has been achieved at the sacrifice of truth, and it seems better to admit ignorance and to be guilty of vagueness rather than to blind ourselves to significant problems.

IMPLICATIONS OF THE DATA FOR THEORIES OF INTELLIGENCE

The doctrine of isolated reflex conduction has been widely influential in shaping current psychological theories. Its assumptions that reactions are determined by local conditions in limited groups of neurons, that learning consists of the modification of resistance in isolated synapses, that retention is the persistence of such modified conditions, all make for a conception of behavior as rigidly departmentalized. Efficiency in any activity must depend upon the specific efficiency of the systems involved; and, since the condition of one synapse cannot influence that of others, there must be as many diverse capacities as there are independent reflex systems.

The effects of such a theory can be traced in many present-day beliefs. If learning is restricted to particular synapses, there can be no influence of training upon other activities than those actually practiced; any improvement in unpracticed functions must be the result of nervous connections which they have in common with the practiced activities. The rejection of doctrines of formal discipline seems to have been based far more upon such reasoning than upon any convincing experimental evidence.

The doctrine of identical elements has been applied also to the problem of insight. When similarities between two situations are recognized, it is because both call out a basic set of reactions involving identical reflex paths. Thus the application of past habits to new situations is limited to those in which an identity of elements can exist; all other adaptive behavior must be explained by the selection of random activities.

There is no evidence to support this belief in identity of nervous elements. On the contrary, it is very doubtful if the same neurons or synapses are involved even in two similar reactions to the same stimulus. Our data seem to prove that the structural elements are relatively unimportant for integration and that the common elements must be some sort of dynamic patterns, determined by the relations or ratios among the parts of the system and not by the specific neurons activated. If this be true, we cannot, on the basis of our present knowledge of the nervous system, set any limit to the kinds or amount of transfer possible or to the sort of relations which may be directly recognized.

The theory of intelligence as an additive function dates from faculty psychology, but it has gained support from theories of localization and reflex structure. These provide no mechanism by which a general capacity could function, other than by modifying the general nutritional level of the neurons. The results of the present experiments lend support to the theory which conceives intelligence as a general capacity, in the same measure that they oppose theories of restricted reflex conduction. The capacity to form and to retain a variety of maze habits and other less well-defined habits seems relatively constant for each individual, dependent upon the absolute quantity of cortical tissue functional and independent of any qualitative differentiation of the cortex or sensorimotor peculiarities of the problems solved. There is an indication that difficult tasks become disproportionately more difficult with decreased cerebral efficiency. Such facts can only be interpreted as indicating the existence of some dynamic function of the cortex which is not differentiated with respect to single capacities but is generally effective for a number to which identical neural elements cannot be ascribed. In this there is close harmony with theories of a general factor determining efficiency in a variety of activities. The diverse results obtained in the studies of problem boxes and brightness discrimination show that this factor is not universally effective. I have pointed out the probable psychological simplicity of these problems and have cited experiments in progress which suggest that when their complexity is increased they likewise reveal at least the severer grades of deterioration. If this is substantiated, it will indicate that the participation of the general factor is determined by the complexity of the functions and is independent of their qualitative diversities.

SUMMARY

The influence of the extent of cerebral destruction in the rat was tested for a variety of functions, including retention of maze habits formed before cerebral insult, and learning and retention of several habits after the insult. The results may be summarized as follows:

1. The capacity to form maze habits is reduced by destruction of cerebral tissue.

2. The reduction is roughly proportional to the amount of destruction.

3. The same retardation in learning is produced by equal amounts of destruction in any of the cyto-architectural fields. Hence the capacity to learn the maze is dependent upon the amount of functional cortical tissue and not upon its anatomical specialization.

4. Additional evidence is presented to show that the interruption of association or projection paths produces little disturbance of behavior, so long as cortical areas supplied by them remain in some functional connection with the rest of the nervous system.

5. The more complex the problem to be learned, the greater the retardation produced by any given extent of lesion.

6. The capacity to form simple habits of sensory discrimination is not significantly reduced by cerebral lesions, even when the entire sensory field is destroyed.

7. This immunity is probably due to the relative simplicity of such habits.

8. The capacity to retain is reduced, as is the capacity to learn.

9. The maze habit, formed before cerebral insult, is disturbed by lesions in any part of the cortex. The amount of reduction in efficiency of performance is proportional to the extent of injury and is independent of locus.

10. Reduction in ability to learn the maze is accompanied

by many other disturbances of behavior, which cannot be stated quantitatively but which give a picture of general inadequacy in adaptive behavior.

11. No difference in behavior in maze situations could be detected after lesions in different cerebral areas, and the retardation in learning is not referable to any sensory defects.

12. A review of the literature on cerebral function in other mammals, including man, indicates that, in spite of the greater specialization of cerebral areas in the higher forms, the problems of cerebral function are not greatly different from those raised by experiments with the rat.

From these facts the following inferences are drawn:

1. The learning process and the retention of habits are not dependent upon any finely localized structural changes within the cerebral cortex. The results are incompatible with theories of learning by changes in synaptic structure, or with any theories which assume that particular neural integrations are dependent upon definite anatomical paths specialized for them. Integration cannot be expressed in terms of connections between specific neurons.

2. The contribution of the different parts of a specialized area or of the whole cortex, in the case of non-localized functions, is qualitatively the same. There is not a summation of diverse functions, but a non-specialized dynamic function of the tissue as a whole.

3. Analysis of the maze habit indicates that its formation involves processes which are characteristic of intelligent behavior. Hence the results for the rat are generalized for cerebral function in intelligence. Data on dementia in man are suggestive of conditions similar to those found after cerebral injury in the rat.

4. The mechanisms of integration are to be sought in the dynamic relations among the parts of the nervous system rather than in details of structural differentiation. Suggestions toward a theory of the nature of these forces are presented.

BIBLIOGRAPHY

ADRIAN, E. D. 1923. "The Conception of Nervous and Mental Energy," *Brit. Jour. Psychol.*, Gen. Sec., XIV, 121–25.

BECHTEREW, W. VON. 1911. *Die Funktionen der Nervencentra* (Jena).

BERNHEIMER, ST. 1900. "Die corticalen Sehcentren," *Wien. klin. Wochenschr.*, XIII Jahrg., 955–63.

BIANCHI, L. 1894. "The Functions of the Frontal Lobes," *Brain*, XVIII, 497–522.

———. 1922. *The Mechanism of the Brain and the Function of the Frontal Lobes* (Edinburgh).

BOLTON, J. S. 1903a. "The Function of the Frontal Lobes," *Brain*, XXVI, 215–41.

———. 1903b. "The Histological Basis of Amentia and Dementia," *Arch. of Neurol., London County Asylum*, II, 424–620.

———. 1914. *The Brain in Health and Disease* (London).

BOUMAN, L., und GRÜNBAUM, A. A. 1925. "Experimentelle-psychologische Untersuchungen zur Aphasie und Paraphasie," *Zschr. f. d. ges. Neurol. u. Psychiat.*, XCVI, 481–538.

BROADBENT, W. H. 1872. "On the Cerebral Mechanism of Speech and Thought," *Trans. Roy. Med. Chir. Soc.*, LV, 145–94.

BROWN, T. G. 1914. "On the Nature of the Fundamental Activity of the Nervous Centers," *Jour. Physiol.*, XLVIII, 18–46.

CAMERON, N. 1928. "Cerebral Destruction in Its Relation to Maze Learning," *Psychol. Mono.*, XXXIX, No. 1, 1–68.

CARR, H. A. 1917. "The Alternation Problem. A Preliminary Study," *Jour. Animal Behavior*, VII, 365–84.

CARR, H. A., and WATSON, J. B. 1908. "Orientation in the White Rat," *Jour. Comp. Neurol. and Psychol.*, XVIII, 27–44.

CHIEVITZ, J. H. 1891. "Über das Vorkommen der Area centralis retinae in den vier höheren Wirbelthierklassen," *Arch. f. Anat. u. Entw.*, pp. 311–34.

CHILD, C. M. 1924. *Physiological Foundations of Behavior* (New York).

DETWEILER, S. R. 1922. "Experiments on the Transplantation of Limbs in Amblystoma," *Jour. Exp. Zoöl.*, XXXV, 115–62.

———. 1925. "Co-ordinated Movements in Supernumerary Transplanted Limbs," *Jour. Comp. Neurol.*, XXXVIII, 461–93.

DONALDSON, H. 1924. "The Rat," *Memoirs of the Wistar Institute, No. 6* (2d ed.; Philadelphia).

EBBECKE, U. 1919. *Die kortikalen Erregungen* (Leipzig).

FEUCHTWANGER, E. 1923. "Die Funktionen des Stirnhirns, ihre Pathologie und Psychologie," *Monogr. a. d. Ges. d. Neurol. u. Psychiat.*,
XXXVIII, iv+194.

FLOURENS, P. 1842. *Recherches expérimentales sur les propriétés et les
fonctions du système nerveux* (Paris).

FORTUYN, A. E. B. D. 1914. "Cortical Cell-Laminations of the Brains of
Some Rodents," *Arch. Neur. and Psychiat.* (London), VI, 221–354.

FRANZ, S. I. 1902. "On the Functions of the Cerebrum: 1. The Frontal
Lobes in Relation to the Production and Retention of Simple Sensory-
Motor Habits," *Amer. Jour. Physiol.*, VIII, 1–22.

———. 1907. "On the Functions of the Cerebrum. The Frontal Lobes,"
Arch. of Psychol., No. 2, pp. 1–64.

———. 1911. "On the Functions of the Cerebrum: The Occipital Lobes,"
Psychol. Mono., XIII, No. 56, 1–118.

———. 1915a. "Symptomatological Differences Associated with Similar
Cerebral Lesions in the Insane," *ibid.*, XIX, No. 1, 1–80.

———. 1915b. "Variation in Distribution of the Motor Centers," *ibid.*,
pp. 80–162.

FRANZ, S. I., and LASHLEY, K. S. 1917. "The Retention of Habits by the
Rat after Destruction of the Frontal Portion of the Cerebrum,"
Psychobiol., I, 3–18.

FUCHS, W. "Untersuchungen über das Sehen der Hemianopiker und Hemi-
amblyopiker." *See* Gelb und Goldstein *below*.

GELB, A., und GOLDSTEIN, K. 1920. *Psychologische Analysen hirnpatholo-
gischer Fälle* (Leipzig).

GOLDSTEIN, K. 1923. "Die Topik der Grosshirnrinde in ihrer klinischen
Bedeutung," *Dtsch. Zschr. f. Nervenheilk.*, LXXVII, 7–124.

———. 1924. "Das Wesen der amnestischen Aphasie," *Schweiz. Arch. f.
Neurol. u. Psychiat.*, XV, 163–75.

GOLDSTEIN, K., und GELB, A. 1918. "Über den Einfluss des vollständigen
Verlustes des optischen Vorstellungsvermögens auf das taktile Erken-
nen," *Zschr. f. d. ges. Neurol. u. Psychiat.*, XLI, 1–142.

GOLTZ, F. 1881a. "Über die Verrichtungen des Grosshirns," *Arch. f. d. ges.
Physiol.*, XXVI, 1–49.

———. 1881b. *Über die Verrichtungen des Grosshirns* (Bonn).

HAMILTON, G. V. 1916. "A Study of Perseverance Reactions in Primates
and Rodents," *Behavior Mono.*, III, No. 13, 1–65.

HAMMARBERG, C. 1895. *Studien über Klinik und Pathologie der Idiotie*
(Upsala).

HEAD, H. 1923. "The Conception of Nervous and Mental Energy," *Brit.
Jour. Psychol.*, Gen. Sec., XIV, 126–47.

———. 1926. *Aphasia and Kindred Disorders of Speech* (New York).

HEIDENHAIN, A. 1927. "Beitrag zur Kenntnis der Seelenblindheit,"
Monatschr. f. Psychiat. u. Neurol., LXVI, 61–116.

HERON, W. T. 1922. "The Reliability of the Inclined Plane Problem Box as a Measure of Learning Ability in the White Rat," *Comp. Psychol. Mono.*, I, No. 1, Part I, 1–36.

————. 1924. "Individual Differences in Ability Versus Chance in the Learning of the Stylus Maze," *Comp. Psychol. Mono.*, II, No. 8, 1–60.

HERRICK, C. J. 1926a. *The Brains of Rats and Men* (Chicago).

————. 1926b. *Fatalism or Freedom* (New York).

HITZIG, E. 1884. "Zur Physiologie des Grosshirns," *Archiv. f. Psychiat. u. Nervenheilk.*, XV, 270–75.

————. 1903. "Alte und neue Untersuchungen über das Gehirn," *Archiv f. Psychiat. u. Nervenkr.*, XXXVII, 277–609.

HOLMES, G., and LISTER, W. T. 1916. "Disturbances of Vision from Cerebral Lesions with Special Reference to the Macula," *Brain*, XXXIX, 34–73.

HORSLEY, V. 1907. "Dr. Hughlings Jackson's View of the Function of the Cerebellum," *Brit. Med. Jour.*, I, 803–8.

HUBBERT, H. B., and LASHLEY, K. S. 1917. "Retroactive Association and the Elimination of Errors in the Maze," *Jour. Animal Behavior*, VII, 130–38.

HUNTER, DOROTHY. 1926. "A Study in Localization of a Complex Motor Habit in the Albino Rat." Thesis, University of Minnesota.

HUNTER, W. S. 1922. "Correlation Studies with the Maze with Rats and Humans," *Comp. Psychol. Mono.*, I, No. 1, Part II, 37–56.

HUNTER, W. S., and RANDOLPH, V. 1924. "Further Studies on the Reliability of the Maze with Rats and Humans," *Jour. Comp. Psychol.*, IV, 431–42.

JOHNSON, H. M. 1913. "Audition and Habit Formation in the Dog," *Behavior Mono.*, Vol. II, No. 8, pp. iv+78.

————. 1914. "Visual Pattern-Discrimination in the Vertebrates. II. Comparative Visual Acuity in the Dog, the Monkey and the Chick," *Jour. Animal Behavior*, IV, 340–61.

————. 1916a. "Visual Pattern-Discrimination in the Vertebrates. III. Effective Differences in Width of Visible Striae for the Monkey and the Chick," *ibid.*, VI, 169–88.

————. 1916b. "Visual Pattern-Discrimination in Vertebrates. V. A Demonstration of the Dog's Deficiency in Detail-Vision," *ibid.*, pp. 205–21.

KAPPERS, C. U. A. 1917. "Further Contributions on Neurobiotaxis. No. IX. An Attempt to Compare the Phenomena of Neurobiotaxis with Other Phenomena of Taxis and Tropism. The Dynamic Polarization of the Neuron," *Jour. Comp. Neurol.*, XXVII, 261–98.

KLÜVER, H. 1927. "Visual Disturbances after Cerebral Lesions," *Psychol. Bull.*, XXIV, 316–58.

KÖHLER, W. 1921. *Intelligenzprüfungen an Menschenaffen* (Berlin).

KOFFKA, K. 1925. *The Growth of the Mind* (New York).

KUO, Z. Y. 1922. "The Nature of Unsuccessful Acts and Their Order of Elimination in Animal Learning," *Jour. Comp. Psychol.*, II, 1–27.

LANDIS, C. 1924. "Studies of Emotional Reactions. II. General Behavior and Facial Expressions," *Jour. Comp. Psychol.*, IV, 447–511.

LASHLEY, K. S. 1912. "Visual Discrimination of Size and Form in the Albino Rat," *Jour. Animal Behavior*, II, 310–31.

———. 1915. "Notes on the Nesting Activities of the Noddy and Sooty Terns," *Carnegie Inst. Washington Pub. No. 211*, pp. 61–83.

———. 1917. "The Accuracy of Movement in the Absence of Excitation from the Moving Organ," *Amer. Jour. Physiol.*, XLIII, 169–94.

———. 1918. "A Simple Maze: With Data on the Relation of the Distribution of Practice to the Rate of Learning," *Psychobiol.*, I, 353–67.

———. 1920. "Studies of Cerebral Function in Learning," *ibid.*, II, 55–135.

———. 1921a. "Studies, ... II. The Effects of Long Continued Practice upon Cerebral Localization," *Jour. Comp. Psychol.*, I, 453–68.

———. 1921b. "Studies, ... III. The Motor Areas," *Brain*, XLIV, 255–86.

———. 1922. "Studies, ... IV. Vicarious Function after Destruction of the Visual Areas," *Amer. Jour. Physiol.*, LIX, 44–71.

———. 1923. "Temporal Variation in the Function of the Gyrus Precentralis in Primates," *ibid.*, LXV, 585–602.

———. 1924a. "Studies, ... V. The Retention of Motor Habits after the Destruction of the So-called Motor Areas in Primates," *Arch. Neurol. and Psychiat.*, XII, 249–76.

———. 1924b. "Studies, ... VI. The Theory that Synaptic Resistance Is Reduced by the Passage of the Nervous Impulse," *Psychol. Rev.*, XXXI, 369–375.

———. 1926. "Studies, ... VII. The Relation between Cerebral Mass, Learning, and Retention," *Jour. Comp. Neurol.*, XLI, 1–58.

LASHLEY, K. S., and BALL, JOSEPHINE. 1929. "Spinal Conduction and Kinaesthetic Sensitivity in the Maze Habit," *Jour. Comp. Psychol.*, IX, 70–106.

LASHLEY, K. S., and FRANZ, S. I. 1917. "The Effects of Cerebral Destruction upon Habit Formation and Retention in the Albino Rat," *Psychobiol.*, I, 71–139.

LASHLEY, K. S., and MCCARTHY, DOROTHEA A. 1926. "The Survival of the Maze Habit after Cerebellar Injuries," *Jour. Comp. Psychol.*, VI, 423–33.

LIGGETT, J. R. 1928. "An Experimental Study of the Olfactory Sensitivity of the White Rat," *Genetic Psychol. Mono.*, III, No. 1, 1–64.

LOEB, J. 1884. "Die Sehstörungen nach Verletzungen der Grosshirnrinde," *Arch. f. d. ges. Physiol.*, XXXIV, 67–172.

———. 1886. "Beiträge zur Physiologie des Grosshirns," *ibid.*, XXXIX, pp. 265–346.

———. 1902. *Comparative Physiology of the Brain and Comparative Psychology* (New York).

———. 1912. "Die Bedeutung der Anpassung der Fische an den Untergrund für die Auffassung des Mechanismus des Sehens," *Zentbl. f. Physiol.*, XXV, 1015–17.

LUCIANI, L. *Human Physiology* (New York).

LUCIANI, L., und SEPPILI, G. 1886. *Die Functions-Localisation auf der Grosshirnrinde* (Translated by Fraenkel; Leipzig).

McDOUGALL, W. 1903. "The Nature of Inhibitory Processes within the Nervous System," *Brain*, LII, 153–91.

———. 1923. *Outline of Psychology* (New York).

MARIE, P. 1906. "Revision de la question de l'aphasie," *Sem. Méd.*, pp. 241–47.

MARIE, P., et CHATELIN, C. 1914–15. "Les troubles visuel dus aux lésions des voies optiques intracérébrales et de la sphère visuelle corticale dans les blessures du crâne par coup de feu," *Rev. neurol.*, XXVIII, 882–925.

MAST, S. O., and PUSCH, L. C. 1924. "Modifications of an Amoeba," *Biol. Bull.*, XLVI, 55–59.

MILES, W. R. 1927. "The Narrow-Path Elevated Maze for Studying Rats," *Proc. Soc. Exp. Biol. and Med.*, XXIV, 454–56.

MINKOWSKI, M. 1911. "Zur Physiologie der Sehsphäre," *Arch. f. d. ges. Physiol.*, CXLI, 171–327.

———. 1917. "Étude physiologique des circonvolutions rolandique et parietal," *Arch. Suisse de Neurol. et Psychiat.*, I, 389–459.

MONAKOW, C. VON. 1905. *Gehirnpathologie* (Wien).

———. 1914. *Die Lokalization im Grosshirn* (Wiesbaden).

MOUTIER, F. 1908. *L'aphasie de Broca* (Paris).

MÜLLER, H. 1911. "Zur Ökonomie des Lernens bei geistesschwachen Personen," *Klinick f. psych. u. nerv. Krankh.*, VI, 121–57.

MUNK, H. 1881. *Über die Funktionen der Grosshirnrinde* (Berlin).

———. 1890. "Of the Visual Area of the Cerebral Cortex, and Its Relation to Eye Movements," *Brain*, XIII, 45–70.

———. 1909. *Über die Funktionen von Hirn und Rückenmark* (Berlin).

PANICI, L. 1903. "Sulla sede del centro psichico della visione nelle scimmie," *Arch. per le scienze. med.*, XXVII, 141–72.

PAVLOV, I. P. 1927. *Conditioned Reflexes* (Oxford Press).

PETERSCN, J. 1917. "The Effect of Length of Blind Alleys upon Maze Learning," *Behavior Mono.*, III, No. 4, 1–53.

PICK, A. 1913. *Die agrammatischen Sprachstörungen* (Berlin).

PIÉRON, H. 1923. *Le cerveau et le pensée* (Paris).

PIKE, F. H. 1918. "Remarks on von Monakow's *Die Lokalisation im Grosshirn,*" *Jour. Comp. Neurol.*, XXIX, 485–509.

POPPELREUTER, W. 1917. *Die psychischen Schädigungen durch Kopfschuss* (Leipzig).

———. 1923. "Zur Psychologie und Pathologie der optischen Wahrnehmung," *Zschr. f. d. ges. Neurol. u. Psychiat.*, LXXXIII, 26–152.

SCHÄFER, E. A. "The Cerebral Cortex," in *Schäfer's Textbook of Physiology* (Edinburgh).

SCHÄFER, E. A., and BROWN, SANGER. 1888. "An Investigation into the Functions of the Occipital and Temporal Lobes of the Monkey's Brain," *Philos. Trans. Roy. Soc.*, Ser. B, CLXXIX, 303–29.

SHERRINGTON, C. S. 1906. *The Integrative Action of the Nervous System* (New York).

SLONAKER, J. R. 1897. "A Comparative Study of the Area of Acute Vision in Vertebrates," *Jour. Morphol.*, XIII, 445–503.

SMITH, E. M. 1912. "Some Observations Concerning Color Vision in Dogs," *Brit. Jour. Psychol.*, V, 119–203.

SPEARMAN, C. 1927. *The Abilities of Man* (New York).

STONE, C. P. 1922. "The Congenital Sexual Behavior of the Young Male Albino Rat," *Jour. Comp. Psychol.*, II, 95–153.

———. 1923. "Further Studies of Sensory Functions in the Activation of Sexual Behavior in the Young Male Albino Rat," *ibid.*, III, 469–73.

STONE, C. P., and NYSWANDER, D. B. 1927. "The Reliability of Rat Learning Scores from the Multiple-T Maze as Determined by Four Different Methods," *Ped. Sem. and Jour. Genetic Psychol.*, XXXIV, 497–524.

SZYMANSKI, J. S. 1918. "Versuche über die Fähigkeit der Hunde zur Bildung von optischen Association," *Arch. f. d. ges. Physiol.*, CLXXI, 317–23.

THORNDIKE, E. L. 1913. *Educational Psychology* (New York).

———. 1926. *The Measurement of Intelligence* (New York).

TOLMAN, E. C. 1924. "The Inheritance of Maze Learning Ability in Rats," *Jour. Comp. Psychol.*, IV, 1–18.

———. 1925a. "Purpose and Cognition: The Determiners of Animal Learning," *Psychol. Rev.*, XXXII, 285–97.

———. 1925b. "Behaviorism and Purpose," *Jour. Philos.*, XXII, 36–41.

TREDGOLD, A. F. 1903. "Amentia (Idiocy and Imbecility)," *Arch. Neurol.*, London County Asylums, II, 328–423.

VINCENT, S. B. 1915. "The White Rat and the Maze Problem. II. The Introduction of an Olfactory Control," *Jour. Animal Behavior*, V, 140–57.

VITZOU, A. N. 1893. "Effets de l'ablation totale des lobes occipitaux sur la vision chez le chien," *Arch. de physiol., norm. et pathol.*, V, 688–98.

——. 1897. "Le néoformation des cellules nerveuses dans le cerveau du singe consécutive à l'ablation complète des lobes occipitaux," *ibid.*, IX, 29–43.

——. 1898. "Récupération de la vue perdue à la suite d'une première ablation totale des lobes occipitaux chez les singes," *Proc. IV Int. Cong. Physiol.; Jour. Physiol.*, XXIII, 57–59.

WARDEN, C. J., and WARNER, L. H. 1928. "The Sensory Capacities and Intelligence of Dogs, with a Report on the Ability of the Noted Dog 'Fellow' to Respond to Verbal Stimuli," *Quar. Rev. Biol.*, III, 1–28. 1–28.

WASHBURN, M. F. 1916. *Movement and Mental Imagery* (New York).

WATSON, J. B. 1907. "Kinaesthetic and Organic Sensations: Their Rôle in the Reactions of the White Rat to the Maze," *Psychol. Mono.*, VIII, No. 2 (vi+100).

——. 1909. "Some Experiments Bearing upon Color Vision in Monkeys," *Jour. Comp. Neurol. and Psychol.*, XIX, 1–28.

WEAVER, H. E., and STONE, C. P. 1928. "The Relative Ability of Blind and Normal Rats in Maze Learning," *Jour. Genetic Psychol.*, XXXV, 157–76.

WEISS, P. 1924. "Die Funktion transplantierter Amphibienextremitäten. Aufstellung einer Resonanztheorie der motorischen Nerventätigkeit auf Grund abgestimmter Endorgane," *Arch. f. mikrosk. Anat.*, CII, 645–72.

——. 1926. "The Relation between Central and Peripheral Co-ordination," *Jour. Comp. Neurol.*, XL, 241–52.

YERKES, R. M. 1916. "A New Method of Studying Ideational and Allied Forms of Behavior in Man and Other Animals," *Proc. Nat. Acad. Sci.*, II, 631–34.

——. 1927. "The Mind of a Gorilla," *Genetic Psychol. Mono.*, II, Nos. 1–2, 1–193.

INDEX

Adrian, 166
Amnestic aphasia, 156
Association areas, 6
Auditory region, 51

Ball, 114, 136
Behavior Research Fund, vii
Bechterew, 145, 150
Bernheimer, 145, 148
Bianchi, 8–9, 10, 131, 142, 148–50, 155
Blindness, 111; psychic, 144, 147
Bolton, 7
Bouman, 153–55
Brightness discrimination. *See* Tests
Broadbent, 6
Brown, 149, 161

Cameron, 74
Capacity to learn, 27. *See also* Lesions
Carr, 29, 136
Cerebral function, 70, 142, 151 ff.; dog, 142 ff.; mass factor in, 1; monkey, 149 ff.; specificity of, 122
Cerebral lesions. *See* Lesions
Cerebral localizations, 161. *See also* Lesions
Chatelin, 151
Child, 167
Correlations, 21 ff., 61, 68 ff., 107; analysis of, 65; spurious, 62, 101

Deterioration, 35; degree of, 61 ff.; learning in, 81 ff.; nature of, 132 ff.; permanence of, 48 ff.; types of, 116 ff.
Detweiler, 159
Diaschisis, 101, 103
Donaldson, 48
Double-platform box. *See* Tests
Dynamic theories, 164

Ebbecke, 164
Ebbinghaus, 77
Equipotentiality, 25
Equilibrium, disturbance of, **25**

Feuchtwanger, 9
Flechsig, 6
Flourens, 4, 148

Fortuyn, 50
Franz, 9, 24, 86–87, 120, 132, 135, 149–50, 162
Fuchs, 153

Gall, 6
Gelb, 112, 153
Gestalt school, 3, 13
Goldstein, 112, 154–55
Goltz, 4, 11, 142, 144, 148–49
Grünbaum, 153–55

Hamilton, 29
Hammarberg, 7
Head, 153–55, 162, 165–66
Heidenhain, 156
Heron, 20
Herrick, xi, 1, 50, 69
Hitzig, 6, 10, 142, 145, 148
Holmes, 151
Hunter, 20, 28, 87, 121, 132

Incline box. *See* Tests
Identical elements, 172
Institute for Juvenile Research, vii
Intelligence: criteria of, 12; in dog, 148; in monkey, 150; theories of, neurological, 3 ff.; theories of, psychological, 1 ff.; *see* Theories

Johnson, 143, 149

Kappers, 125, 167–68
Klüver, 10, 152
Koffka, 3
Kuo, 137

Lashley, 16, 18, 24–25, 28, 60, 86–87, 101, 103, 114, 120, 122, 132, 135–37, 148, 158–59, 162, 170
Learning: ability, 109; curves, 82 ff.; initial, 111
Lesions, 132, Plates I–XI; effect of, 27, 55, 76, 86 ff., 100; extent of, 61 ff.; 74, 121, Plates I–XI; subcortical, 64, 105
Liggett, 113
Lister, 151
Localization: of habit, 86 ff.; variation in, 24

Locus of injury, 122; influence on retardation, 49, 91, 117, 141
Loeb, 5, 11, 142, 144, 148–49, 161
Luciani, 142, 144

McCarthy, 114–15
McDougall, 1, 164
Marie, 151, 153
Mass function, 25, 88
Mast, 13
Maze. See Tests
Mental energy, 164
Methods: anatomical, 16; graphic, 18; reliability of, 20; special, 89; statistical, 18; surgical, 16
Minkowski, 142, 146–47, 162
Monakow, 6, 10, 24, 49, 102, 140, 148, 153, 155
Motor region, 53
Moutier, 153–54
Müller, 72
Munk, 5–6, 10, 112, 123, 142–43, 147, 149

Nervous energy, 164
Neural mechanisms, 157
Neural organization, 167
Neural potency, 166
Nyswander, 20

Orbeli, 143
Osler, William, vii

Panici, 150
Pavlov, 127, 142–43, 146, 149
Peterson, 137
Pick, 153
Piéron, 151, 165
Pike, 166
Poppelreuter, 88, 147, 153, 163
Pusch, 13

Randolph, 20
Retardation, 132 ff., 138 ff.; degree of, 74
Retention. See Tests

Schäfer, 149
Sense-privation, 110; audition, 113; motor, 115; olfaction, 112; touch, 112; vision, 110
Sensoripsychic, 9

Sensory spheres, 6
Seppili, 142, 144
Shenger-Krestovnikova, 143
Sherrington, 125
Slonaker, 143
Smith, 143
Somesthetic region, 52
Spearman, 2, 10
Specific shock, 24
Spencer, 163
Stone, 20, 158
Synapse, in retention, 125 ff.
Szymanski, 143

Tests: brightness discrimination, 32, 75: averages, 42–43, correlations (see Correlations), data, 59 ff., habits, 45 ff., individual records, 36 ff., initial learning, 46, results, 120 ff., 132, retention of, 33, 46, 76 ff., 100, 111; incline box, 34, 75: averages, 42–43, individual records, 36 ff., results, 120 ff., 132 ff.; maze (I, II, III, IV), 30 ff.: averages, 42–43, correlations (see Correlations), data, 51 ff., 58 ff. habit, 136, 138, individual records, 36 ff., learning of, 30–32, 106, results, 120 ff., retention, 32, 76 ff., 91 ff., 100, 111, reversal, 32
Theories of intelligence, 1 ff., 172; aggregate, 2; aggregation, 5; configuration hypothesis, 3; dynamic, 4, 164; localization, 6; reduplication, 129; reflex, 163; two-factor, 2; unit factory, 1
Thorndike, 2, 10–11, 123, 125
Tolman, 1, 19–20
Transitional region, 54
Treffer method, 78

Vicarious function, 24
Vincent, 113
Visual area, 53
Visual mechanisms, 143, 149
Visuo-psychic areas, 7
Visuo-sensory areas, 7
Vitzu, 145, 150

Warden, 143
Warner, 143
Washburn, 136
Watson, 109, 136, 149
Weiss, 159

Yerkes, 29

PLATES I–IV

Diagrams of the Lesions in the Series of Cases Trained in a Variety of Problems after Brain Injury, Arranged in the Order of Magnitude of the Lesions. For Each Diagram the Figure to the Left is the Identification Number of the Case Used in the Tables and Text; That to the Right, the Percentage of the Cortex Destroyed

PLATE I

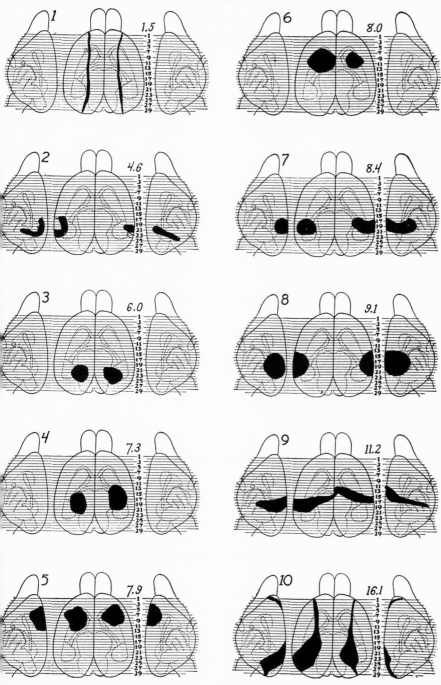

PLATE II

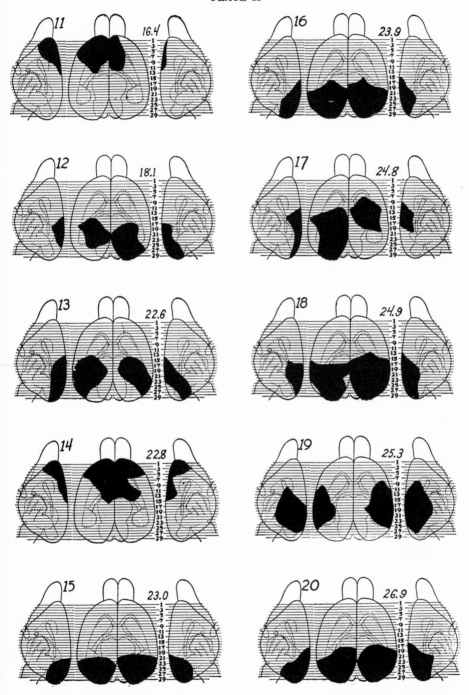

PLATE III

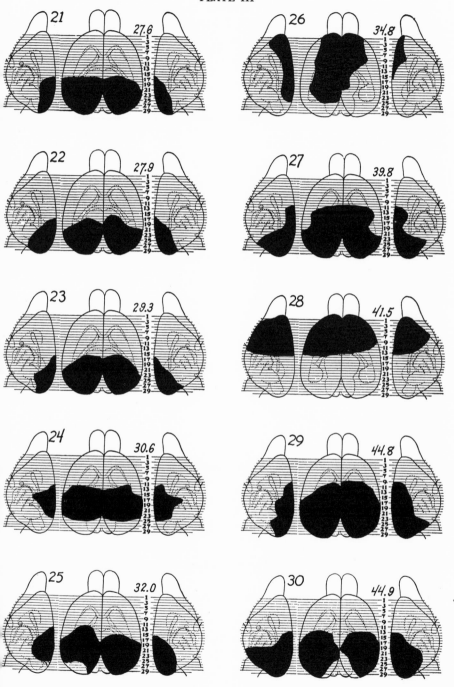

PLATE IV

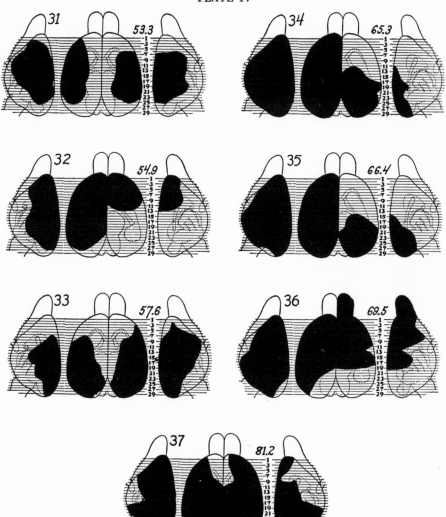

PLATES V–X

Diagrams of the Lesions in the Series of Cases Tested for Postoperative Retention of the Habit of Maze III, Arranged as Plates I–IV

PLATE V

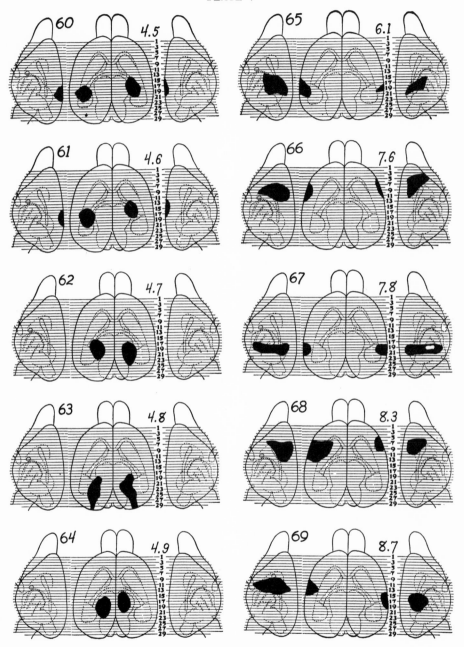

PLATE VI

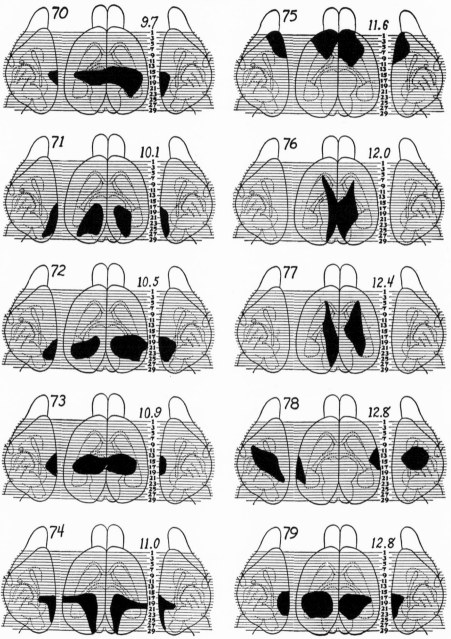

PLATE VII

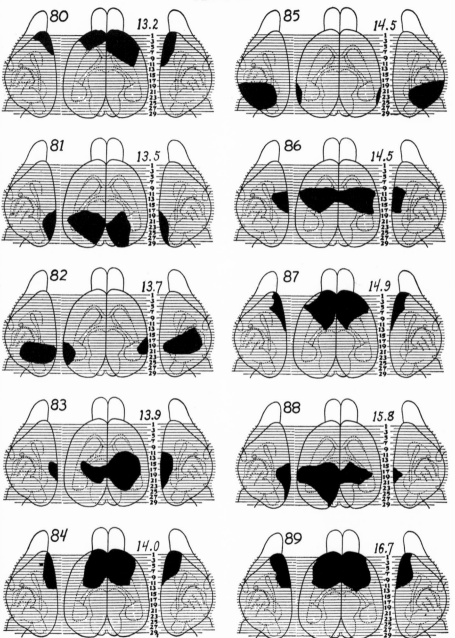

PLATE VIII

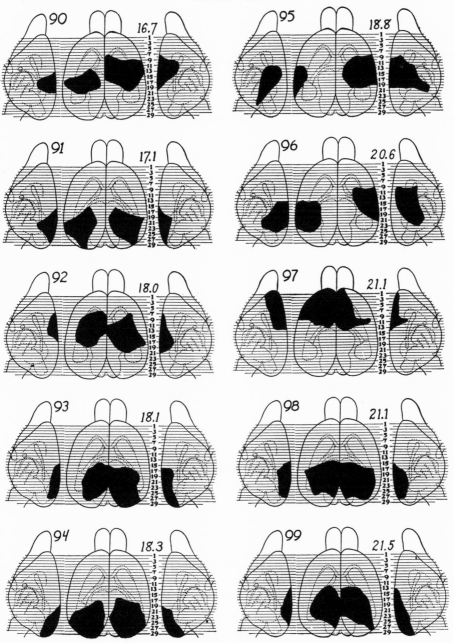

PLATE IX

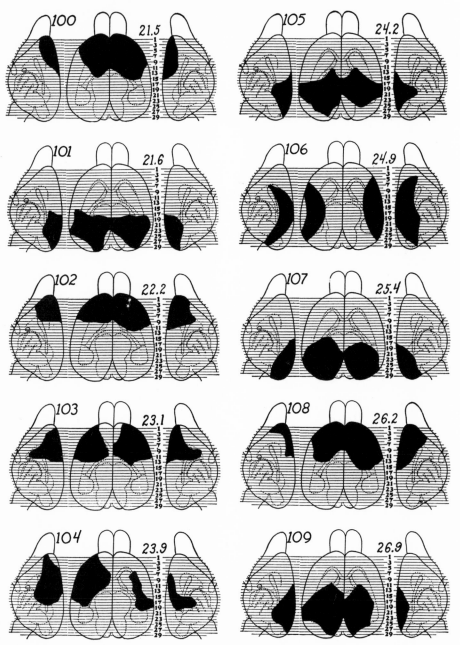

PLATE X

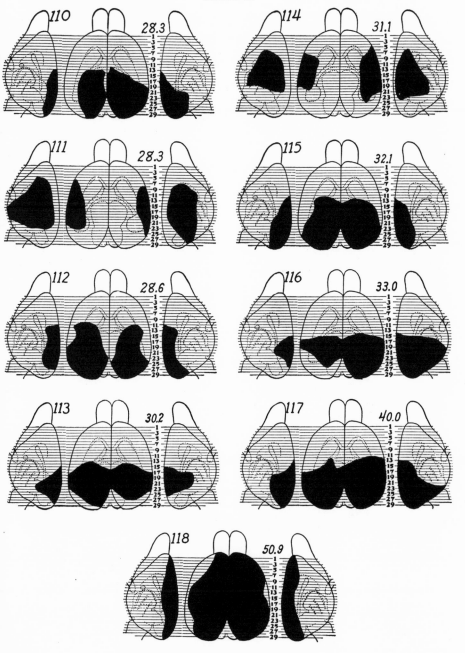

PLATE XI

Figures 125–30: Diagrams of Lesions in Blind Animals. Figures 131–33: Diagrams of Lesions in Animals Which Developed Vestibular Infection. Figures 134 and 135: Progressive Lesions

PLATE XI

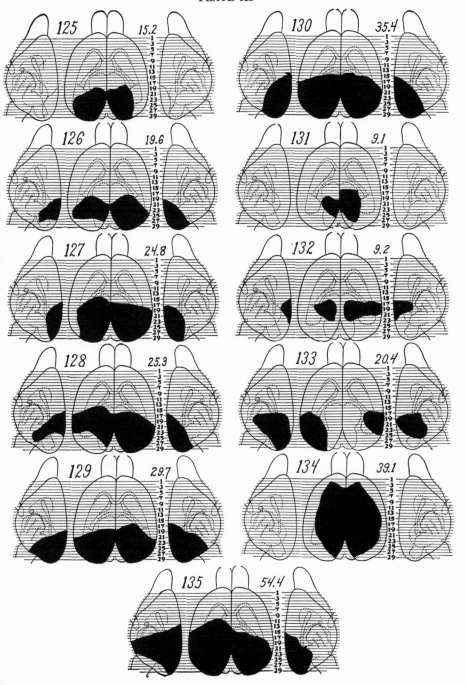